# FUTURE

## English for Results

# 1

## TESTS and TEST PREP
with **Exam***View*® *Assessment Suite*

Jennifer Gaudet
Daniel S. Pittaway

Series Consultants
Beatriz B. Díaz
Ronna Magy
Federico Salas-Isnardi

**Future 1 Tests and Test Prep**



Pearson Education, 10 Bank Street, White Plains, NY 10606

**Staff credits**: The people who made up the *Future 1 Tests and Test Prep* team, representing editorial, production, design, and manufacturing, are: Rhea Banker, Aerin Csigay, Mindy De Palma, Nancy Flaggman, Irene Frankel, Katherine Keyes, Linda Moser, Barbara Sabella, and Julie Schmidt

**Cover design:** Rhea Banker
**Cover photo:** Kathy Lamm/Getty Images
**Text design:** Barbara Sabella
**Text composition:** Rainbow Graphics
**Text font:** 13 pt Minion

**Photo credits:** All original photography by David Mager. Page 1(TL) Blend Images/Jupiterimages, (TM) Redchopsticks Collect/agefotostock, (BM) Shutterstock, (BR) Shutterstock; 3 Corbis/Jupiterimages; 7(T) Shutterstock, (B) Shutterstock; 11(TL) Shutterstock, (TM) Kayte M. Deioma/PhotoEdit, (TR) Jeff Greenberg/PhotoEdit; 20(L) Dreamstime.com, (R) Shutterstock; 26(2) BigStockPhoto.com, (3) Shutterstock, (4) Shutterstock; 31(BL) Shutterstock, (BM) iStockphoto.com, (BR) Shutterstock; 36 Shutterstock; 40 Shutterstock; 41(BL) Photos.com, (BM) iStockphoto.com, (BR) iStockphoto.com; 43 iStockphoto.com; 46(L) Shutterstock, 50 Shutterstock; 60(TL) Shutterstock, (TM) Shutterstock, (TR) Shutterstock, (BL) Shutterstock, (BM) Michael Newman/PhotoEdit, (BR) Shutterstock; 66 Michael Newman/PhotoEdit; 69 Shutterstock; 70 (TL) Shutterstock, (TM) iStockphoto.com, (TR) Dreamstime.com, (BL) iStockphoto.com, (BM) Shutterstock, (BR) Shutterstock; 79 Shutterstock; 86(1) Jim Zuckerman/Corbis, (2) Kent Wood/Photo Researchers, Inc., (3) Shutterstock, (4) Shutterstock; 89 Shutterstock; 90(TL) Will & Deni McIntyre/Corbis, (TM) Blend Images/Jupiterimages, (TR) Royalty-Free Division/Masterfile; 97 Shutterstock; 99 iStockphoto.com; 114 Shutterstock; 116(1) Lon C. Diehl/PhotoEdit, (2) iStockphoto.com, (3) Shutterstock, (4) iStockphoto.com; 118 Shutterstock.

ISBN-13: 978-0-13-240878-3
ISBN-10: 0-13-240878-3



Printed in the United States of America
1 2 3 4 5 6 7 8 9 10 —CRS— 12 11 10 09

# Contents

# Introduction

Welcome to *Future 1 Tests and Test Prep.* This package (containing a book, audio CD, and e-CD) provides all the assessment tools you need:

- The **Test Prep** section at the beginning of the book contains test-taking strategy worksheets and a sample test.
- The **Printed Unit Tests** in the book test students' mastery of the content presented in the Student Book units. The audio CD accompanies these tests.
- The **Exam***View®* ***Assessment Suite*** on the e-CD offers a wealth of additional ways to assess students. Teachers can create their own unique tests, print, or customize already prepared, multilevel unit tests in addition to midterm and final tests.

## TEST PREP

Many adult ESL students are unfamiliar with standardized tests. The Test Prep section contains reproducible worksheets that will prepare students for both the printed unit tests in this book and for any standardized tests they may have to take, such as the CASAS Life and Work Series. You will find the following worksheets on pages viii–xvi:

- How to Use an Answer Sheet
- Instructions for the Sample Unit Test
- Sample Unit Test (Listening, Grammar, and Life skills sections)
- Answer Key and Audio script for the Sample Test (the teacher may choose not to distribute this to students)
- Standardized Tests—Practice Questions
- Test-Taking Strategies

You can distribute the worksheets to your class over a period of time (for example, one or two pages a week). Alternatively, you can wait until students are close to the time they will test or post-test and then go over all the material in one session.

To administer the sample unit test:

- Go over the Instructions for the Sample Unit Test worksheet with your class.
- Make copies of the sample unit test and of the blank answer sheet on page 119. Distribute the copies to your students. Have them bubble in their test answers on the answer sheet.
- The audio for the sample listening questions can be found on the audio CD, Tracks 2–4. Play each track twice, pausing for 10 to 20 seconds between each play.
- Check answers using the answer key and the audio script for the sample test on page xiv.

The sample test (with the exception of the grammar section) is similar in format and content to the CASAS Life and Work series tests, but not identical to them. The CASAS website—www.casas.org—offers additional information, such as practice test questions, that you may find useful.

## PRINTED UNIT TESTS

The are 12 printed unit tests in this test booklet. They are designed to assess how well students have mastered the material presented in each unit of the Student Book. Each test contains the following sections:

- Listening
- Grammar
- Vocabulary
- Life Skills
- Reading

The listening, vocabulary, life skills, and reading sections of the tests emulate the look and feel of the CASAS Life and Work Reading and Listening Series tests. All the sections use multiple choice format, modeling the format students will encounter in standardized tests.

### Listening

The listening section includes a variety of item types and is divided into three parts: Listening I, Listening II, and Life Skills I. (Life Skills I does not appear in every test.)

In the **Listening I** and **Life Skills I** sections, students listen to test items and look at the answer choices on the test page. The answer choices are usually pictures.

In **Listening II**, both the questions and the answer choices are on the audio CD. There are two types of questions. In the first type, students hear a statement or question, and they have to choose the appropriate response to that statement or question. In the second type, the students hear a short conversation, and they have to answer a comprehension question about that conversation.

The directions and the answer choices appear on the Listening II test page. This is different from the CASAS test, where students are not given answer choices to look at for these question types. In other words, students bubble in their answers on the answer sheet, but they do not see the questions or answer choices in print. If your students need extra support, give them the second page of the test, the Listening II page, when you distribute the test. But if you wish to emulate CASAS more closely, you should omit the second page of the test.

### Grammar

Students are asked to complete short conversations that contain examples of the grammar points presented in the unit.

### Vocabulary

Students identify pictures of vocabulary items that were presented in the vocabulary lesson(s) of the unit.

### Life Skills

The life skills section may include both listening and reading items. In the Life Skills listening section (Life Skills I), students look at three different pictures and listen to a sentence or conversation, and then choose the correct picture. In the Life Skills reading section (either Life Skills I or Life Skills II), students read a brief text or look at pictures. Then they answer questions about the text or pictures.

### Reading

Students read a short paragraph that reflects the grammar and themes covered in the unit and then answer comprehension questions about it.

### Answer Keys and Audio Scripts

You will find an Answer Key and an Audio Script for each printed unit test at the back of this book. The answer key is an answer sheet with the correct answers for the test bubbled in. It also provides diagnostic information about each test question.

### Administering and Scoring Printed Unit Tests

To administer a printed unit test:

- Find the test you want in this book and photocopy it.
- Decide whether or not you want students to look at the Listening II page as they take the test (see the Listening II section). Either include or omit the Listening II page when you distribute the test.
- Make copies of the blank answer sheet on page 119 and distribute them to your students. Ask students to bubble in their test answers on the answer sheet.
- Start with the listening section of the test. Locate the appropriate audio track on the audio CD. We recommend that you play each track twice, pausing for 10 to 20 seconds between each play. This will approximate how listening is presented on standardized tests.
- Each 33-item test is designed to take 25–30 minutes to administer.

To score a printed unit test:

- Collect your students' bubbled-in answer sheets.
- Locate the answer key for the test at the back of the book. To create a scoring mask, photocopy the answer key and punch a hole in each bubbled-in answer.

When you lay this scoring mask over a student answer sheet, you can easily see if the student has bubbled in the correct answer. If the bubble is not filled in, then simply mark an X on the unmarked bubble with a colored pencil.

- Count the number of correctly bubbled in answers on the student's answer sheet. Each correct answer is worth 3 points. To calculate a percentage score for your students, multiply the number of correct answers by three and add one point.

The answer key provides the objective that each item tests, along with the lesson and page number in the Student Book where the material was presented. If a student answers a particular item incorrectly, you will then know which competency the student has missed and/or which lesson he or she may need further practice in.

## EXAM*VIEW*® *ASSESSMENT SUITE*

The **Exam***View*® *Assessment Suite* can be used either to supplement the printed unit tests or in place of them. With **Exam***View*, you can create or customize your own tests for students. Alternatively, you can choose to simply print out unit, midterm, or final tests that have already been prepared for you and administer them to your class.

For detailed information on how to install the **Exam***View* software and use it to create, customize, and print out tests, please refer to the *TO THE TEACHER* PDF located on the *Future 1* **Exam***View*® *Assessment Suite* e-CD. The installation instructions in the back of this book will tell you how to find this document.

### Exam*View*® Unit Tests

The prepared **Exam***View* unit tests are designed to address the needs of multilevel classes. Each unit test is offered at three different levels: **pre-level, on-level,** and **above-level**. You can choose to divide your class into three different groups and to administer a different version of a test to each group simultaneously. You can also use different versions of a test to diagnose a student's level.

The **Exam***View* unit tests have the same general structure as the printed unit tests in the book, with a series of multiple choice questions that test listening, grammar, vocabulary, life skills, and reading skills. However, the **Exam***View* unit tests do not follow the CASAS testing format as closely as the printed unit tests do. Another difference is that there are two separate types of tests for each unit. The first is a Listening Test, in PDF format, and the second is an **Exam***View* Test, containing grammar, vocabulary, life skills, and reading items.

The Listening Tests are offered in PDF format to make them easier for teachers to administer. There are separate pre-level, on-level, and above-level PDFs for each listening test. All three levels share the same audio. They also share the same basic structure: students listen to longer conversations (similar to the listenings in the Student Book) and then answer comprehension questions about them.

Meanwhile, grammar, vocabulary, life skills, and reading skills are tested in the **Exam***View* unit tests. There are separate pre-level, on-level, and above-level **Exam***View* tests for each unit. Again, all three levels share the same basic structure.

### Exam*View*® Midterm and Final

The **Exam***View* midterm and final tests are offered at on-level only in order to provide an objective, standardized way to assess all your students at the halfway point and at the end of the course. They have a total of 66 items each. The Midterm tests the content presented in Units 1–6 and the Final covers Units 7–12. As with the unit tests, the Midterm and Final Listening Tests are in PDF format, and grammar, vocabulary, life skills, and reading items are in (on-level only) **Exam***View* question banks.

### Administering and Scoring Exam*View* Tests

To administer an **Exam***View* test:

- You can administer **Exam***View* tests via computer or simply print them out and distribute them to your students.

- If you want to administer a multilevel unit test, divide your class into pre-level, on-level, and above-level groups.
- Locate the appropriate PDFs and **Exam***View* tests on the e-CD. For example, if you wanted to administer the pre-level tests for Unit 1, you would print out the pre-level listening test PDF and the pre-level **Exam***View* test for Unit 1. (Please refer to the *TO THE TEACHER* PDF for more information on how to select the PDFs or tests you need.)
- Distribute the tests to your students. (Note: the answer keys for the **Exam***View* tests print out automatically at the end of the test. Make sure you do not distribute the answer key to your students along with the test!)
- If you are printing out tests for your students, make copies of the blank answer sheet on page 119. Distribute two copies to each student. One copy is for the Listening Test, and the other copy is for the **Exam***View* Test.
- Start with the Listening Test. Play the appropriate audio tracks for the test. Have students fill in the correct number of bubbles on the first answer sheet (usually, for six test items). Then collect the listening answer sheets.
- Next, administer the **Exam***View* test for the unit. Have students bubble in the second answer sheet. Collect the answer sheets when students are finished.
- Allow 25–30 minutes for students to complete the Listening Test and the **Exam***View* test for each unit. Allow 50–60 minutes for a midterm or final.

To score an **Exam***View* test:

- Collect your students' bubbled-in answer sheets.
- Locate the answer keys for the test. The answer keys and audio script for each listening test are in PDF format in the same folder as the listening test. For the unit listening tests, there is a pre-level listening answer key, an on-level listening answer key, and an above-level listening answer key. Note that there is only one audio script for all three levels of the unit tests. The answer keys for the **Exam***View* tests will print out automatically at the end of each test, as noted above.
- Count the number of correctly bubbled in answers on each student's answer sheets. Add the scores of the Listening Test and the **Exam***View* test together. Then score the **Exam***View* unit tests as you would a printed unit test. For the 66-item midterm or final test, multiply the number of correct answers by 3, add 2 free points, and divide the result by 2 to get a percentage score.

You can find detailed diagnostic information about each test item in the answer keys, including the following:

- Level of Difficulty (DIF): Pre-level, On-level, or Above-Level
- Reference (REF): student book level and unit being tested
- Learning objective (OBJ): the learning objective of the item (as found in the *Scope & Sequence*/Student Book unit lesson)
- National standard (NAT): the CASAS competency being tested, if applicable
- Skill (SKL): the skill being tested (listening, grammar, vocabulary, life skills, or reading)

As with the printed unit test answer keys, you can use this diagnostic information to determine which competencies and/or lessons your students need more practice in.

## HOW TO USE AN ANSWER SHEET

For many tests, you use an answer sheet to mark, or bubble in, your answers. You must use a #2 pencil. You do not mark your answers on the test. A machine may score your answers. The machine reads and records the pencil marks on the answer sheet.

First, you need to fill in some personal information on the answer sheet.

Here is an example of the answer sheet in this book:

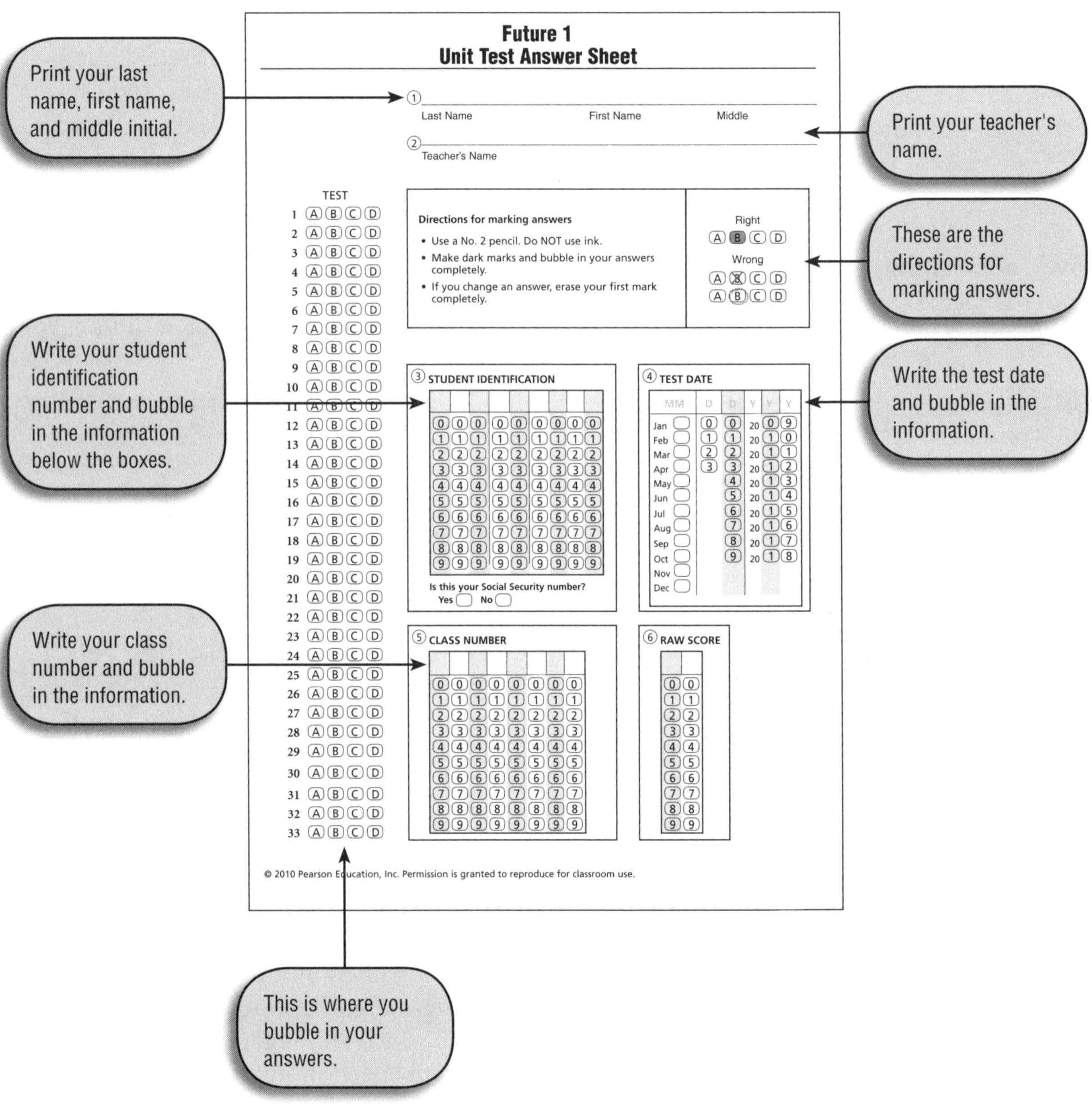

## INSTRUCTIONS FOR THE SAMPLE UNIT TEST

This sample test is like the unit tests in this book. It has listening, grammar, and life skills questions. Follow the directions carefully.

### Listening Section

All the questions in the listening section have three answer choices. You will hear each question two times. Here are examples of the three types of listening questions:

**Example 1:** You listen and choose the correct picture.
**You will hear:** *It's a desk.*

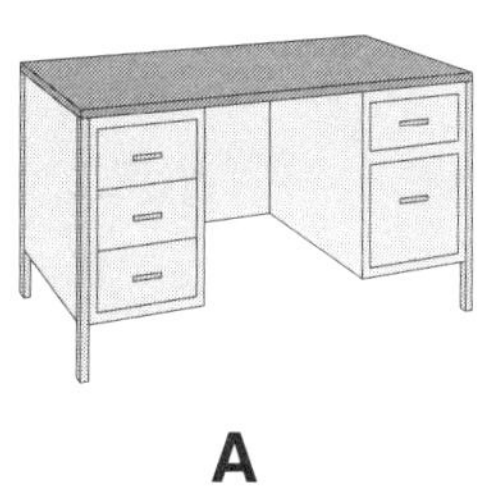

A

B

C

—correct answer: **A**

**Example 2:** You listen and choose the correct response to the statement or question.
**You will hear:** *Can I borrow a pen?*

A. It's a cell phone.
B. Turn off the computer.
C. Sure.

—correct answer: **C**

**Example 3:** You listen to a conversation and choose the correct answer to a question about it.

**You will hear:** **F:** *Who is he?*
**M:** *He's a student.*

*Who is the man?*

A. He's a student.
B. He's a principal.
C. He's a teacher.

—correct answer: **A**

### Grammar and Life Skills Sections

The questions in the grammar section have three answer choices. You choose the correct answer to complete a conversation. The questions in the life skills section have four answer choices. You read or look at a picture and then answer a question about it.

# SAMPLE UNIT TEST

## LISTENING I

*(Track 2)* **Look at the pictures and listen. What is the correct answer: A, B, or C?**

1.

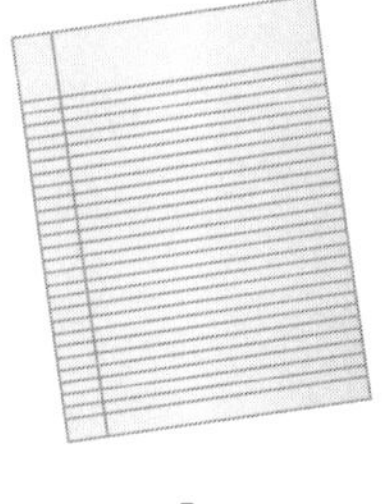

**A**

**B**

**C**

2.

**A**

**B**

**C**

## LISTENING II

***(Track 3)* Listen to the question and three answers. What is the correct answer: A, B, or C?**

**3.** A. It's a cell phone.
B. Turn off the computer.
C. Sure.

**4.** A. They're cell phones.
B. Sure.
C. Don't look at the book.

***(Track 4)* Listen to the conversation. Then listen to the question and three answers. What is the correct answer: A, B, or C?**

**5.** A. The office.
B. The computer lab.
C. The dictionary.

**6.** Who is the man?
A. He's a student.
B. He's the office assistant.
C. He's the teacher.

## GRAMMAR

### Complete each conversation. What is the correct answer: A, B, or C?

**7. A:** Anita doesn't understand.
**B:** OK. Please help ______.

A. her
B. us
C. me

**8. A:** Is ______ your cell phone?
**B:** Yes, it is.

A. these
B. that
C. those

# LIFE SKILLS

## Read. What is the correct answer: A, B, C, or D?

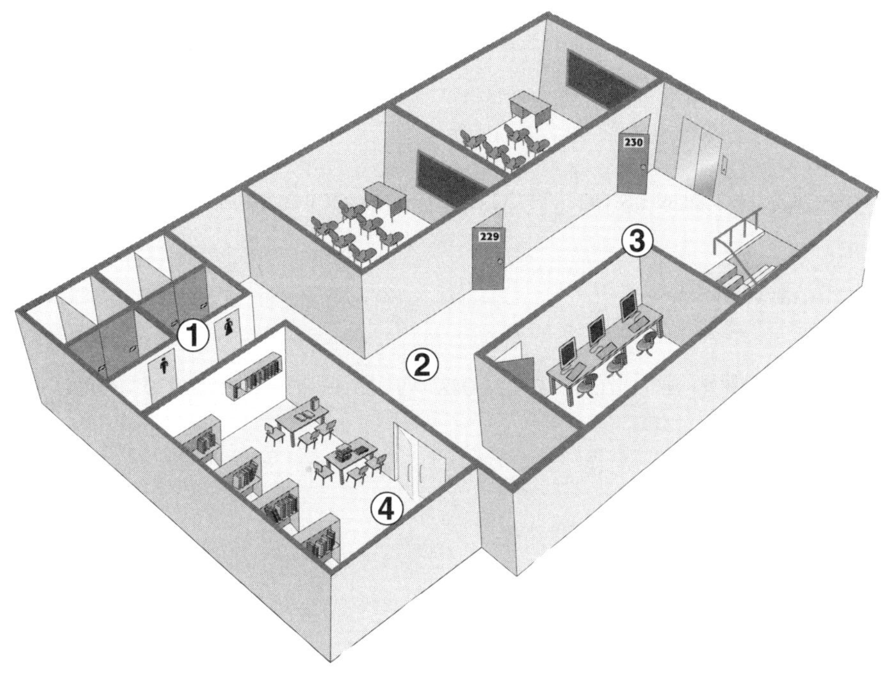


**9.** What is ①?

A. It's a cafeteria.

B. It's an elevator.

C. It's a library.

D. It's a restroom.

**10.** Where is the computer lab?

A. It's next to the cafeteria.

B. It's next to the restroom.

C. It's across from the classroom.

D. It's next to the office.

## ANSWER KEY AND AUDIO SCRIPT FOR THE SAMPLE UNIT TEST

### Answer Key:

| | | | | |
|---|---|---|---|---|
| 1. C | 3. C | 5. B | 7. A | 9. D |
| 2. C | 4. A | 6. C | 8. B | 10. C |

### Audio Script:

LISTENING I
(Track 2) Look at the pictures and listen. What is the correct answer: A, B, or C?

1. It's a book.
2. Take out your dictionary, please.

LISTENING II
(Track 3) Listen to the question and three answers. What is the correct answer: A, B, or C?

3. Can I borrow a piece of paper?
   A. It's a cell phone.
   B. Turn off the computer.
   C. Sure.
4. What are these called in English?
   A. They're cell phones.
   B. Sure.
   C. Don't look at the book.

(Track 4) Listen to the conversation. Then listen to the question and three answers. What is the correct answer: A, B, or C?

5. **F:** Is the computer lab open?
   **M:** Yes, it is.

   What is open?
   A. The office.
   B. The computer lab.
   C. The dictionary.
6. **F:** Who is he?
   **M:** He's the teacher.

   Who is the man?
   A. He's a student.
   B. He's the office assistant.
   C. He's the teacher.

## STANDARDIZED TESTS: PRACTICE QUESTIONS

Many standardized tests begin with a practice page. Here is an example of a practice page. Read through the questions below and make sure you understand how to answer them.

When you take a standardized test, find the practice page. It says *Practice.* Look for the practice answer box on the answer sheet. Use a pencil. Bubble in your answer. Ask the tester for help if you do not understand the directions. When the test begins, you are not allowed to talk. You cannot ask for or give help.

### READING TEST

#### Practice 1

Here's a quarter.

#### Practice 2

| Sun. | Mon. | Tues. | Wed. | Thurs. | Fri. | Sat. |
|---|---|---|---|---|---|---|
| | computer class | | English class | | | |

When is the English class?

A. It's on Monday.
B. It's on Tuesday.
C. It's on Wednesday.
D. It's on Thursday.

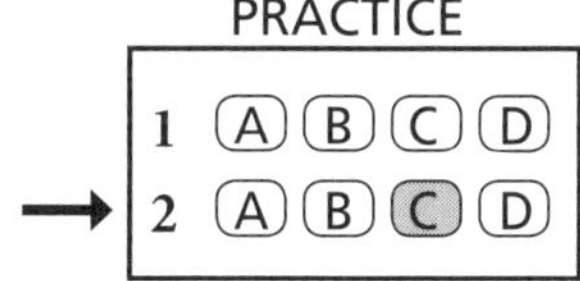

## TEST-TAKING STRATEGIES

### Preparing to Take a Test

- Get a lot of sleep the night before the test.
- Eat a meal or snack before the test.
- Bring two sharpened #2 pencils.
- Bring a pencil eraser.
- Bring a ruler or a blank piece of paper.
- Arrive early to the testing room.
- Make sure you can easily see and hear the tester.
- Turn off your cell phone.
- Try to relax and do your best! Good luck!

### Taking a Test

- As soon as you start a test section, look through the section to see how many questions there are.
- Don't spend too much time on one question. If you don't know the answer, guess and then move on to the next item. You can circle the item number and come back to it at the end if you have time.
- For a listening test: Look at the answer choices for the question. Then listen to the directions and the question. Remember that for some questions, both questions and answer choices may be on the CD. You will hear the questions and the answer choices.
- For all other test sections: Read the material. Read the question carefully. Read all the answer choices.
- Think: Which is the best answer? Look at the answer choices again. Eliminate answers you know are not correct.
- Choose the best answer.
- Make sure you mark your answer on the correct line on the answer sheet. Use a ruler to help you, or use a blank piece of paper to cover the lines below the line you are working on.
- Check each time that you bubble in the circle on the correct line for the question you are answering.
- Do not change the first answer you mark unless you are sure that it is wrong.
- Erase completely any answers you have changed. Fill in only ONE answer on each line. Erase all extra marks on your answer sheet.
- When you finish, if there is time, always recheck your answers.
- If you cannot answer many questions, it is OK. Raise your hand. Tell the tester. You may be excused from taking the rest of the test.

NAME ____________________

# Unit 1 Test

## LISTENING I

***(Track 5)*** **Look at the pictures and listen. What is the correct answer: A, B, or C?**

1.

Mariam

**A**

Yun Hee

**B**

Dora

**C**

2.

**A**

**B**

**C**

NAME ______________________________

## LISTENING II

***(Track 6)*** **Listen to the question and three answers. What is the correct answer: A, B, or C?**

**3.** A. She is from Mexico.
B. I'm from Poland.
C. Yes, I am.

**4.** A. I'm Miguel. I'm from El Salvador.
B. Oh, you're right.
C. That's Anh. She's from Vietnam.

***(Track 7)*** **Listen to the conversation. Then listen to the question and three answers. What is the correct answer: A, B, or C?**

**5.** A. It's easy.
B. It's friendly.
C. It's hard.

**6.** A. She's from Somalia.
B. She's from Russia.
C. She's from China.

## LIFE SKILLS I

***(Track 8)* Look at the pictures and listen. What is the correct answer: A, B, or C?**

7.

(Mr.) Mrs. Ms. Miss
First Name: Matias
Last Name: Silva

A

(Mr.) Mrs. Ms. Miss
First Name: Andres
Last Name: Hernandez

B

(Mr.) Mrs. Ms. Miss
First Name: Karol
Last Name: Boruta

C

8.

V-E-R-A

A

B-E-L-L-A

B

S-A-R-A

C

NAME ______________________________

## GRAMMAR

### Complete each conversation. What is the correct answer: A, B, or C?

9. **A:** Who's that?
   **B:** That's Mr. Eta. ______ from Ethiopia.
   A. He's
   B. I'm
   C. She's not

10. **A:** So, you and Lin are in English 2.
    **B:** No. ______ in English 2. We're in English 3.
    A. He isn't
    B. We aren't
    C. They aren't

11. **A:** Mrs. Jones is the teacher.
    **B:** Yes. ______ from England.
    A. She's
    B. He's not
    C. I'm

12. **A:** Where are Viktor and Galina?
    **B:** ______ here today. They're absent.
    A. We're not
    B. They're not
    C. She's not

13. **A:** Kim is from China.
    **B:** No, she ______ from China. She's from Korea.
    A. isn't
    B. aren't
    C. is

14. **A:** Moon and Ethan are in English 2.
    **B:** Yes. ______ smart.
    A. He is
    B. We are
    C. They are

15. **A:** English 3 is hard!
    **B:** ______ hard. It's easy!
    A. It isn't
    B. They aren't
    C. It's

**16. A:** How are Tina and Paulo?
**B:** They______ great.

A. is
B. 's
C. 're

**17. A:** How is English 2?
**B:** ______ good. The teacher isn't helpful.

A. He isn't
B. She isn't
C. It isn't

**18. A:** Sorry I'm late.
**B:** It's OK. You ______ late.

A. is
B. is not
C. are not

**19. A:** That's not Sammy.
**B:** Oh, you're right. That's Jean-Pierre. ______ from Haiti.

A. She
B. He's
C. They're

**20. A:** How is your class?
**B:** ______ interesting.

A. She's
B. He's
C. It's

**21. A:** My name is Ivan. I'm from Russia.
**B:** Oh. ______ from Russia. I'm from Poland.

A. He's not
B. I'm not
C. It's not

**22. A:** ______ a student.
**B:** No. I'm a teacher!

A. I am
B. You are
C. It is

**23. A:** How is the teacher?
**B:** He's great. ______ friendly.

A. He is
B. He isn't
C. She's

NAME ______________________

# VOCABULARY

**Read. What is the correct answer: A, B, C, or D?**

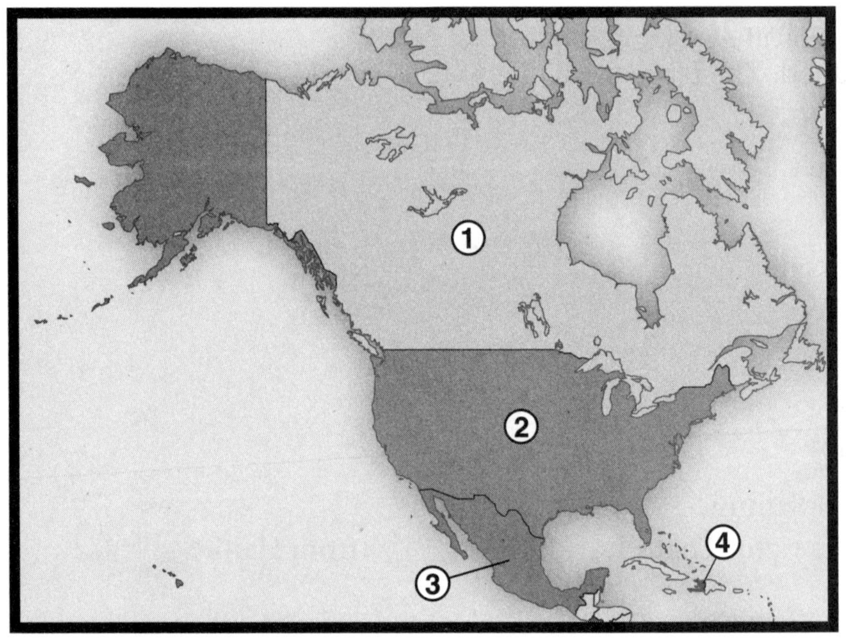


**24.** Karen is from Canada.

A. ①

B. ②

C. ③

D. ④

**25.** Hector is from Mexico.

A. ①

B. ②

C. ③

D. ④

**Read. What is the correct answer: A, B, C, or D?**

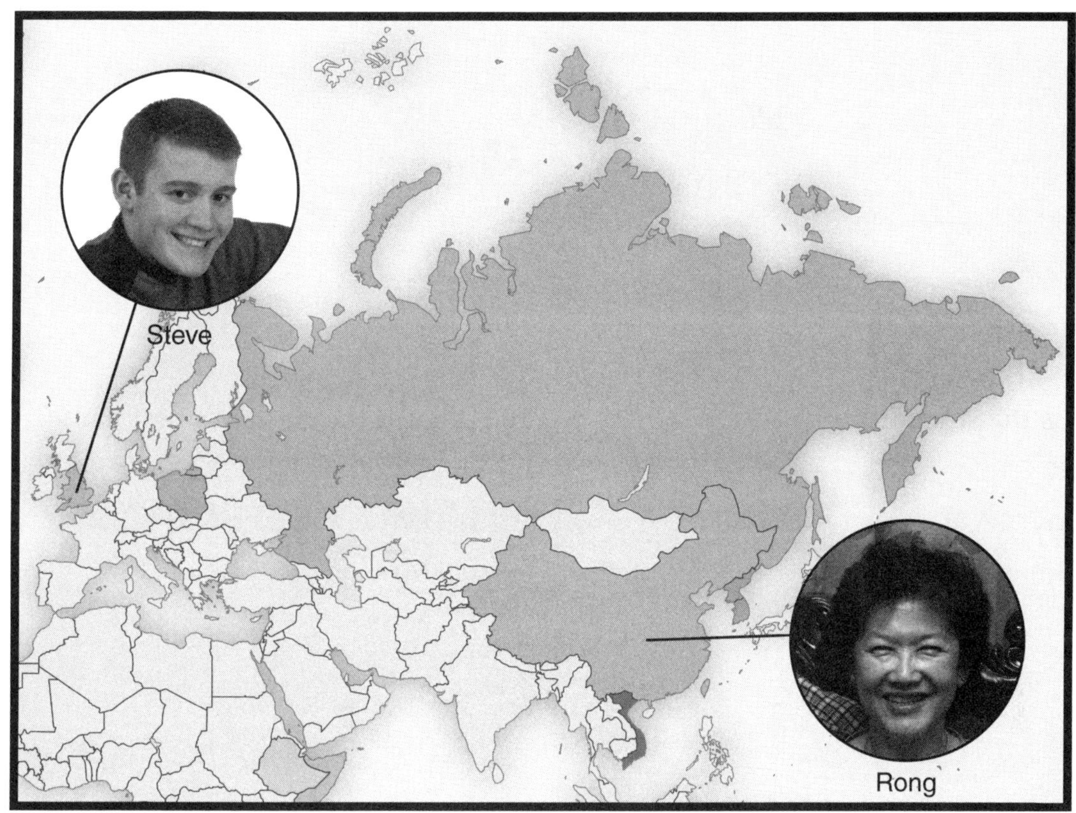


**26.** Where are you from, Rong?

A. I'm from China.
B. I'm from Ethiopia.
C. I'm from Poland.
D. I'm from Haiti.

**27.** Where is Steve from?

A. He's from Brazil.
B. He's from Vietnam.
C. He's from England.
D. He's from Somalia.

NAME______________________________

# LIFE SKILLS II

**Read. What is the correct answer: A, B, C, or D?**

Mr. (Mrs.) Ms. Miss
First Name: Carolina
Last Name: Perez

**28.** What is the student's title?

A. Mr.
B. Mrs.
C. Ms.
D. Miss

**29.** What is the student's first name?

A. Carolina
B. Perez
C. Mrs.
D. Miss

## Read. What is the correct answer: A, B, C, or D?

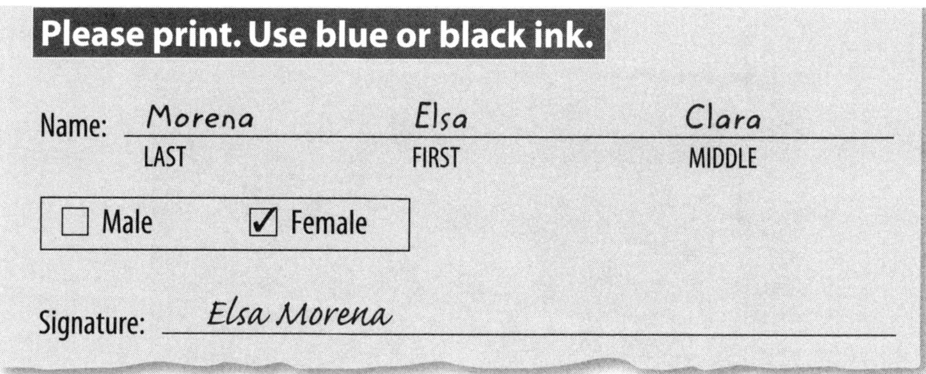
Please print. Use blue or black ink.

Name: Morena (LAST) Elsa (FIRST) Clara (MIDDLE)

☐ Male ☑ Female

Signature: Elsa Morena

**30.** What names are in the signature?

A. the person's first name and middle name
B. the person's first name and last name
C. the person's middle name and last name
D. the person's first name, middle name, and last name

# READING

## Read. What is the correct answer: A, B, C, or D?

Mrs. Gand is a teacher at Northwest Adult School. She's from Canada. She's the teacher for English 1. The students in English 1 are from Vietnam, Mexico, and Somalia. They think the class is good. Mrs. Gand is helpful. She's friendly.

**31.** Where is Mrs. Gand from?

A. Canada
B. Mexico
C. Vietnam
D. Somalia

**32.** What class are the students in?

A. Vietnam, Mexico, and Somalia
B. Canada
C. English 1
D. Northwest Adult School

**33.** How is Mrs. Gand?

A. She isn't good.
B. She's a student.
C. She's helpful.
D. She isn't friendly.

NAME ______________________________

# Unit 2 Test

## LISTENING I

**(*Track 9*) Look at the pictures and listen. What is the correct answer: A, B, or C?**

1.

**A**

**B**

**C**

2.

**A**

**B**

**C**

# LISTENING II

***(Track 10)* Listen to the question and three answers. What is the correct answer: A, B, or C?**

**3.** A. Thomas is a student.
B. Oh, that's interesting.
C. I'm a nurse.

**4.** A. I'm a caregiver.
B. I work at a factory.
C. No, I'm not.

***(Track 11)* Listen to the conversation. Then listen to the question and three answers. What is the correct answer: A, B, or C?**

**5.** A. the man
B. the woman
C. the man and the woman

**6.** A. No, she's not. She's a cashier.
B. No, she's not. She's an office assistant.
C. Yes, she is.

NAME ____________________

## LIFE SKILLS I

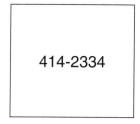

***(Track 12)*** **Look at the numbers and listen. What is the correct answer: A, B, or C?**

7.

**A**

514-2304

**B**

**C**

8.

**A**

(525) 804-2334

**B**

(555) 814-2324

**C**

NAME ______________________________

## GRAMMAR

### Complete each conversation. What is the correct answer: A, B, or C?

**9. A:** Is Dave ______ accountant?
**B:** Yes, he is.

A. and
B. a
C. an

**10. A:** ______ teachers?
**B:** Yes, we are.

A. Are you
B. Is he
C. Are they

**11. A:** Is your job hard?
**B:** No, it ______.

A. is
B. isn't
C. aren't

**12. A:** Is Jamal ______?
**B:** Yes, he is.

A. cooks
B. cook
C. a cook

**13. A:** Is he a waiter?
**B:** Yes. He ______ in a restaurant.

A. live
B. work
C. works

**14. A:** Are you office assistants?
**B:** No, we aren't. We ______ in a nursing home.

A. work
B. works
C. lives

**15. A:** Anita and Sherry are child care workers.
**B:** No, they aren't. They are ______.

A. a waitress
B. waitresses
C. a waiter

**16. A:** Is Mary a homemaker?
**B:** Yes, ______.

A. she isn't
B. they are
C. she is

**17. A:** Are Marcela and Gabrielle nurses?
**B:** Yes. They ______ at Greenview Hospital.

A. lives
B. works
C. work

**18. A:** We ______ in Arizona.
**B:** Really? I live in California.

A. live
B. works
C. is

**19. A:** Carlos is a teacher, right?
**B:** No. He's ______.

A. a painter
B. painter
C. painters

**20. A:** Asad works at a store.
**B:** Really? Is he ______ cashier?

A. a
B. and
C. an

**21. A:** Tom and Sue are ______.
**B:** Yes. They work at a store in New York.

A. sales assistant
B. a sales assistant
C. sales assistants

**22. A:** Is she an artist?
**B:** No, ______.

A. she isn't
B. she is
C. she's

**23. A:** ______ housekeepers?
**B:** Yes, they are.

A. Are they
B. They are
C. They aren't

NAME ______________________

## VOCABULARY

### Read. What is the correct answer: A, B, C, or D?

**24.** What do you do?

A. I'm a child care worker.

B. I'm an office assistant.

C. I'm a cook.

D. I'm a cashier.

**Read. What is the correct answer: A, B, C, or D?**

**25.** This is Joanne.

A. She's a waitress.
B. She's an artist.
C. She's a nurse.
D. She's a housekeeper.

NAME ______________________________

**Read. What is the correct answer: A, B, C, or D?**

**26.** He's a painter.

A. ①

B. ②

C. ③

D. ④

**27.** He's a driver.

A. ①

B. ②

C. ③

D. ④

NAME ______________________________

## LIFE SKILLS II

**Read. What is the correct answer: A, B, C, or D?**

Call Mrs. Tanaka at Teriyaki Restaurant about the waitress job. (222) 555-9009

Call Dr. Feldman at Central Hospital about the nurse job. (222) 333-7007

Call Paul Jackson at Robson Accounting about the office assistant job. (222) 444-8766

Call Ms. Mendoza at Play Time Child Care about the child care worker job. (222) 414-5533

**28.** What's the number for Robson Accounting?

A. (222) 555-9009
B. (222) 444-8766
C. (222) 333-7007
D. (222) 414-5533

**29.** What's the number for the child care worker job?

A. (222) 555-9009
B. (222) 444-8766
C. (222) 333-7007
D. (222) 414-5533

**30.** What's the number for Dr. Feldman?

A. (222) 555-9009
B. (222) 444-8766
C. (222) 333-7007
D. (222) 414-5533

**31.** What's the number for the waitress job?

A. (222) 555-9009
B. (222) 444-8766
C. (222) 333-7007
D. (222) 414-5533

# READING

## Read. What is the correct answer: A, B, C, or D?

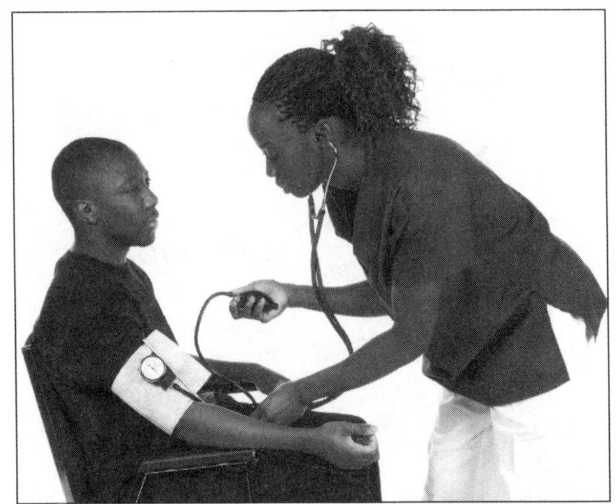

Nancy Banda and Ricardo Sanchez live in San Francisco. Nancy is a nurse. She works at Providence Hospital. Ricardo isn't a nurse. He is a cook. He works in a restaurant. Nancy is good with people. Ricardo isn't good with people. He is good with food!

**32.** Is Nancy a doctor?

A. Yes, she is.

B. No, she isn't. She's a cook.

C. No, she isn't. She's a nurse.

D. No, she isn't. She works at a restaurant.

**33.** What are Ricardo's job skills?

A. He is good with people.

B. He is good with food.

C. He is a nurse.

D. He works in a hospital.

NAME ____________________

# Unit 3 Test

## LISTENING I

***(Track 13)*** **Look at the pictures and listen. What is the correct answer: A, B, or C?**

1.

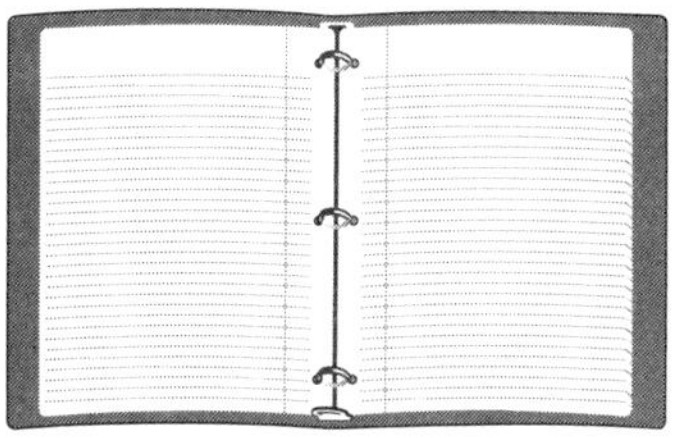

A 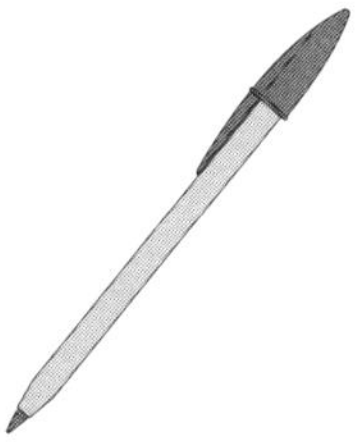 B  C

2.

A  B  C

NAME ______________________________

## LISTENING II

***(Track 14)* Listen to the question and three answers. What is the correct answer: A, B, or C?**

**3.** A. It's a pencil.
B. Take out an eraser.
C. Sure.

**4.** A. They're markers.
B. Sure.
C. Don't look at the exercise.

***(Track 15)* Listen to the conversation. Then listen to the question and three answers. What is the correct answer: A, B, or C?**

**5.** A. The library.
B. The computer lab.
C. The book.

**6.** A. She's the teacher.
B. She's the office assistant.
C. She's the principal.

NAME ____________________

## LIFE SKILLS I

***(Track 16)* Look at the pictures and listen. What is the correct answer: A, B, or C?**

7.

A

B

C

8.

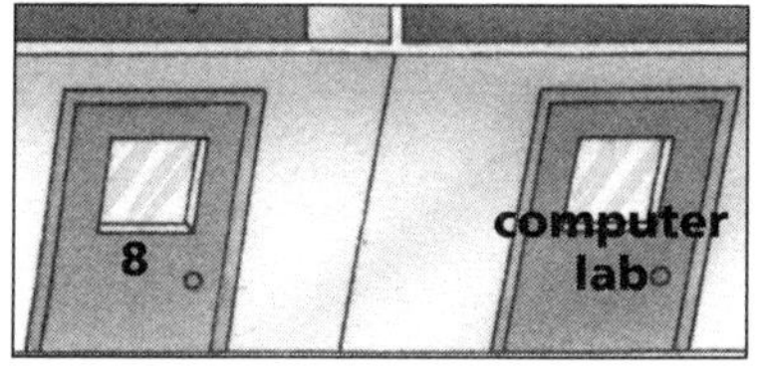


A

B

C

NAME ____________________

## GRAMMAR

### Complete each conversation. What is the correct answer: A, B, or C?

**9. A:** ______ your notebook.
**B:** OK.

A. Take out
B. Don't
C. What

**10. A:** What's ______?
**B:** It's an eraser.

A. they
B. that
C. those

**11. A:** ______ is a great computer.
**B:** Oh, really?

A. This
B. Those
C. We

**12. A:** José doesn't understand.
**B:** OK. Please help ______.

A. him
B. us
C. me

**13. A:** Is ______ your backpack?
**B:** Yes, it is.

A. these
B. this
C. those

**14. A:** What's this?
**B:** ______ a DVD.

A. They're
B. It's
C. We're

**15. A:** Come to class on time.
**B:** Yes, and ______ interrupt the class when you are late.

A. don't
B. do
C. use

16. **A:** ______ are pens.
**B:** Those aren't pens. They're markers.

A. This
B. That
C. These

17. **A:** What are those?
**B:** ______ three-ring binders.

A. They're
B. It's
C. This is

18. **A:** Please don't use a pen. ______ a pencil.
**B:** OK.

A. Open
B. Don't
C. Use

19. **A:** ______ my classmates, Marco and Luisa.
**B:** Hello, Marco. Hello, Luisa.

A. Those are
B. These are
C. This is

20. **A:** Please ______ your dictionary. Open your book.
**B:** Sure.

A. listen
B. don't open
C. don't

21. **A:** ______ a good book.
**B:** These are good books, too.

A. These are
B. Those are
C. This is

22. **A:** Please show ______ your pictures.
**B:** Sure.

A. me
B. I
C. she

23. **A:** Can you help Ivan and Inga?
**B:** Yes, I can help ______.

A. we
B. us
C. them

NAME ___________________________

# VOCABULARY

## Read. What is the correct answer: A, B, C, or D?

①

②

③

④

**24.** What is ①?

A. It's a dictionary.

B. It's a book.

C. It's a three-ring binder.

D. It's a notebook.

**25.** This is a cell phone.

A. ①

B. ②

C. ③

D. ④

## Read. What is the correct answer: A, B, C, or D?

①

②

③

④

**26.** That's a computer.

A. ①
B. ②
C. ③
D. ④

**27.** That's a chair.

A. ①
B. ②
C. ③
D. ④

## LIFE SKILLS II

### Read. What is the correct answer: A, B, C, or D?

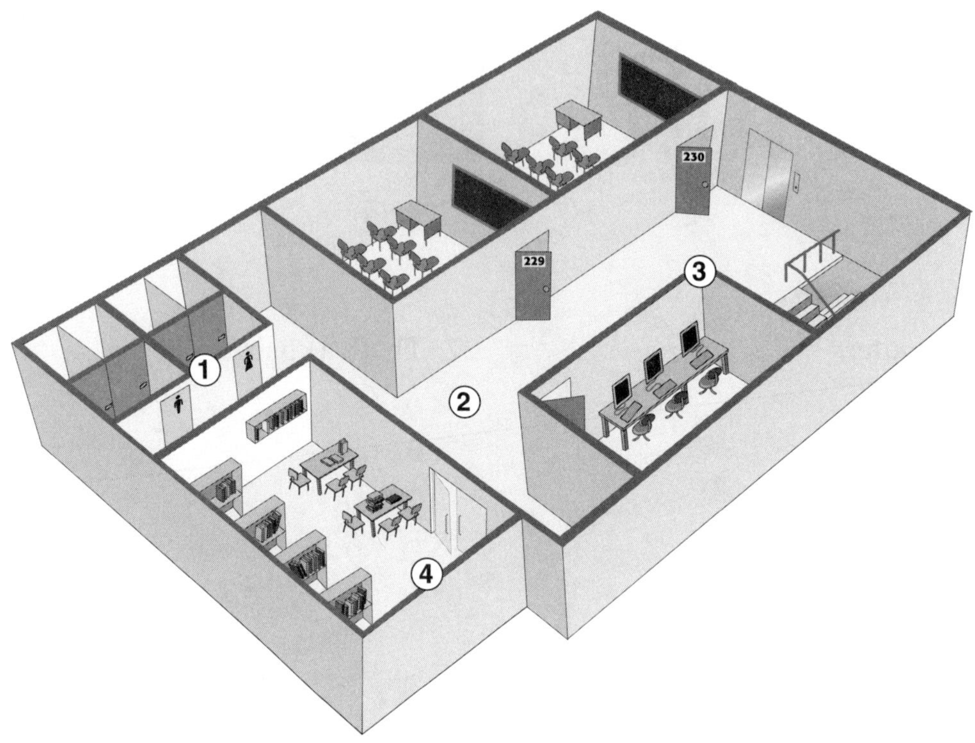


**28.** What is ③?

A. It's a cafeteria.

B. It's an elevator.

C. It's a library.

D. It's a computer lab.

**29.** Where is the restroom?

A. It's next to the cafeteria.

B. It's next to the stairs.

C. It's across from the office.

D. It's next to the library.

**Read. What is the correct answer: A, B, C, or D?**

**LAC Community School** **Registration Form**

Student's Name: Lee (LAST) Jin-Su (FIRST)

Phone: (779) 555-0123 ☐ M ☑ F

Classroom: 205 Subject: English 1

Teacher: Mr. Myers

**30.** What is English 1?

A. a student's name

B. a school

C. a classroom

D. a subject

**31.** What is the teacher's last name?

A. Lee

B. Jin-Su

C. Mr.

D. Myers

# READING

## Read. What is the correct answer: A, B, C, or D?

This is English 1. These are the students in the class. This is the teacher, Ms. Reed. This is her list of *do's* and *don'ts* for the class:

Welcome to English 1. Please:

1. Come to class on time.
2. Bring a pencil and notebook to class.
3. Don't eat in class.
4. Turn off your cell phone.

**32.** What do students bring to class?

A. the teacher

B. a list of *do's* and *don'ts*

C. a pencil and notebook

D. a cell phone

**33.** What do students do in class?

A. eat

B. use their cell phones

C. turn off their cell phones

D. come late

NAME ____________________

# Unit 4 Test

## LISTENING I

***(Track 17)*** **Look at the pictures and listen. What is the correct answer: A, B, or C?**

1.

A

B

C

2.

A

B

C

NAME ______________________

## LISTENING II

***(Track 18)*** **Listen to the question and three answers. What is the correct answer: A, B, or C?**

**3.** A. He's really friendly.
B. No. He has a beard.
C. He's seventy-five.

**4.** A. My sister is here. She's a nurse.
B. She looks like me.
C. He's a gardener.

***(Track 19)*** **Listen to the conversation. Then listen to the question and three answers. What is the correct answer: A, B, or C?**

**5.** A. Pat's uncle
B. Pat's sister
C. Pat's brother

**6.** A. fifth grade
B. sixth grade
C. twelfth grade

NAME ______________________

## LIFE SKILLS I

***(Track 20)*** **Look at the pictures and listen. What is the correct answer: A, B, or C?**

7.

| March | | | | | | |
|---|---|---|---|---|---|---|
| 1 | 2 | 3 | 4 | 5 | 6 | 7 |
| 8 | 9 | 10 | 11 | 12 | 13 | 14 |
| 15 | 16 | (17) | 18 | 19 | 20 | 21 |
| 22 | 23 | 24 | 25 | 26 | 27 | 28 |
| 29 | 30 | 31 | | | | |

**A**

| May | | | | | | |
|---|---|---|---|---|---|---|
| 1 | 2 | 3 | 4 | 5 | 6 | 7 |
| 8 | 9 | 10 | 11 | 12 | 13 | 14 |
| 15 | 16 | (17) | 18 | 19 | 20 | 21 |
| 22 | 23 | 24 | 25 | 26 | 27 | 28 |
| 29 | 30 | 31 | | | | |

**B**

| July | | | | | | |
|---|---|---|---|---|---|---|
| 1 | 2 | 3 | 4 | 5 | 6 | 7 |
| 8 | 9 | 10 | 11 | 12 | 13 | 14 |
| 15 | 16 | (17) | 18 | 19 | 20 | 21 |
| 22 | 23 | 24 | 25 | 26 | 27 | 28 |
| 29 | 30 | 31 | | | | |

**C**

## GRAMMAR

### Complete each conversation. What is the correct answer: A, B, or C?

**8. A:** Hung is in the United States. ______ family is in Vietnam.
**B:** Really?

A. Their
B. His
C. My

**9. A:** Who's Karla?
**B:** I think she's ______ wife.

A. her
B. he's
C. Todd's

**10. A:** Where are Evelia and Antonio's friends from?
**B:** ______ friends are from El Salvador.

A. Their
B. Her
C. Our

**11. A:** How old ______ Shoba's children?
**B:** Seven and twelve.

A. is
B. are
C. have

**12. A:** That's my friend.
**B:** Wow! She ______ long hair!

A. is
B. has
C. have

**13. A:** Who has a beard?
**B:** Tony and Yakof ______ beards.

A. are
B. has
C. have

**14. A:** How old ______ your grandmother?
**B:** She's eighty.

A. is
B. has
C. are

**15. A:** Who's Tom?
**B:** He's ______ brother.

A. she
B. Diana's
C. Diana

**16. A:** This is a picture of my grandfather.
**B:** Wow! He ______ tall!

A. has
B. is
C. are

**17. A:** This is a picture of ______ family.
**B:** You look like your mother!

A. your
B. my
C. I'm

**18. A:** Your sister looks like you.
**B:** Yes. ______ both short!

A. We have
B. We're
C. She has

**19. A:** Mr. Nguyen has a mustache.
**B:** No. He ______ a beard.

A. is
B. have
C. has

**20. A:** Is ______ mother tall?
**B:** No. She's average height.

A. he
B. Michael
C. Michael's

**21. A:** How old ______ you?
**B:** I'm twenty-one.

A. is
B. are
C. am

**22. A:** ______ heavy.
**B:** No, you aren't!

A. I have
B. You're
C. I'm

# VOCABULARY

## Read. What is the correct answer: A, B, C, or D?

**23.** Who's this?

A. Stella's grandfather

B. Stella's daughter

C. Stella's son

D. Stella's wife

**Read. What is the correct answer: A, B, C, or D?**

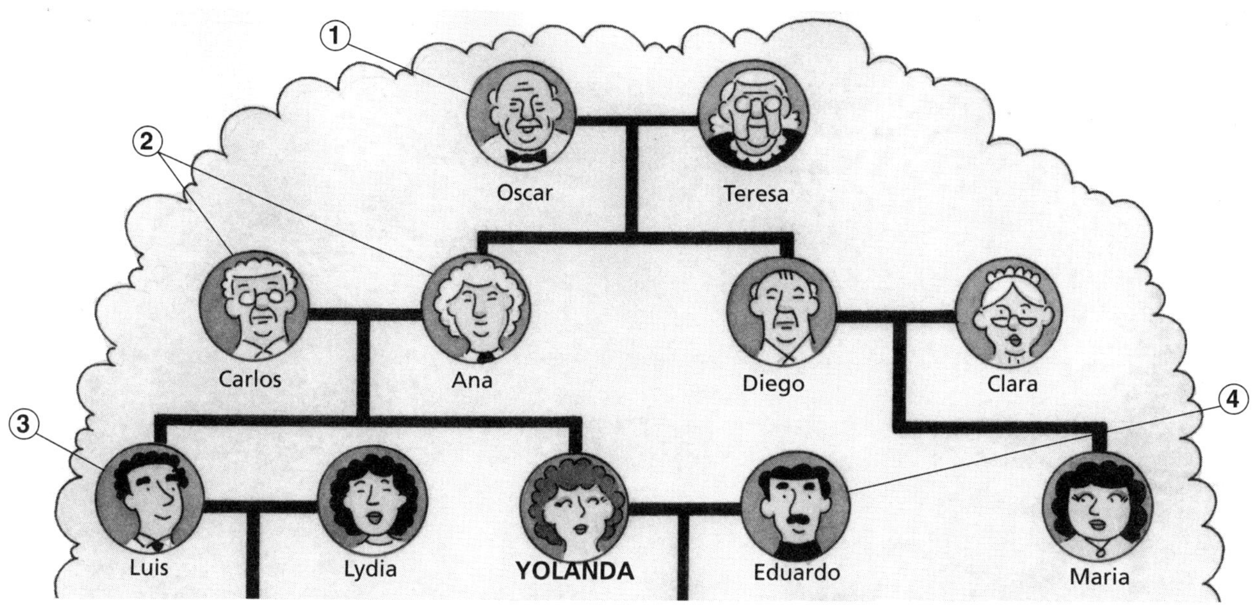


**24.** This is Yolanda's grandfather.

A. ①

B. ②

C. ③

D. ④

**25.** This is Yolanda's brother.

A. ①

B. ②

C. ③

D. ④

**26.** These are Yolanda's parents.

A. ① and ②

B. ②

C. ③

D. ③ and ④

# LIFE SKILLS II

## Read. What is the correct answer: A, B, C, or D?

| November | | | | | | |
|---|---|---|---|---|---|---|
| 1 | 2 | 3 | 4 | 5 | 6 | 7 |
| 8 | 9 | 10 | 11 | 12 | 13 | (14) |
| 15 | 16 | 17 | 18 | 19 | 20 | 21 |
| 22 | 23 | 24 | 25 | 26 | 27 | 28 |
| 29 | 30 | | | | | |

**27.** When is Lupe's birthday?

A. November fourth

B. November fourteenth

C. November fifteenth

D. November twenty-fourth

NAME ______________________

**Read. What is the correct answer: A, B, C, or D?**

| 2-03-78 | 2-13-78 | 9-01-08 | 1-09-08 |
|---|---|---|---|
| ① | ② | ③ | ④ |

**28.** Peter's birthday is February 13, 1978.

A. ①
B. ②
C. ③
D. ④

**29.** The date is September 1, 2008.

A. ①
B. ②
C. ③
D. ④

NAME ____________________

# READING

## Read. What is the correct answer: A, B, C, or D?

Rafael is in the United States. He is twenty-five years old. He is tall. His brothers are in the United States, too. They are tall, too. Rafael's parents and sister are in Mexico. His father is short. He has a mustache. His mother is heavy and short. She has long hair. Rafael's sister has long hair, too. She is tall.

**30.** Who is in the United States?

A. Rafael and his brothers

B. Rafael's father

C. Rafael's mother

D. Rafael's children

**31.** How old is Rafael?

A. 19

B. 25

C. 29

D. 35

**32.** Who is short?

A. Rafael

B. Rafael's brothers

C. Rafael's father and mother

D. Rafael's sister

**33.** What is Rafael's mother like?

A. She is tall.

B. She is average height.

C. She's heavy.

D. She has short hair.

NAME ______________________

# Unit 5 Test

## LISTENING I

***(Track 21)*** **Look at the pictures and listen. What is the correct answer: A, B, or C?**

1.

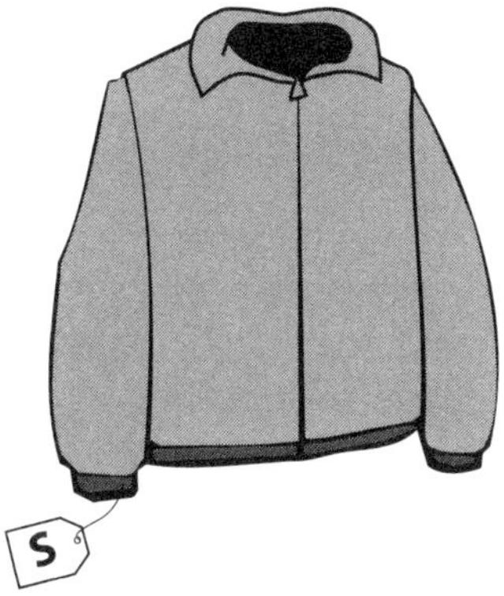

S | L | M

A 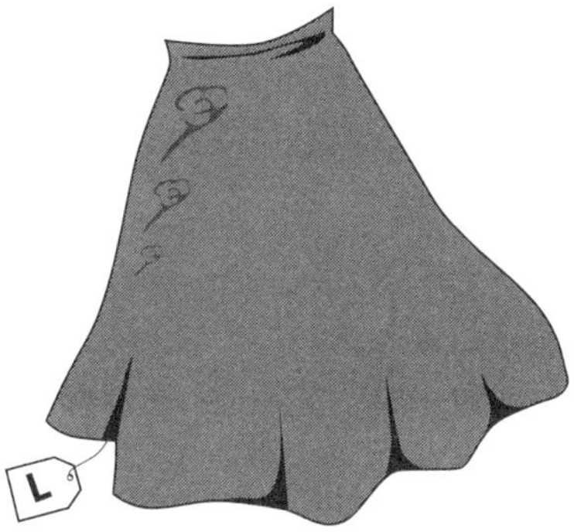 | B  | C

2.

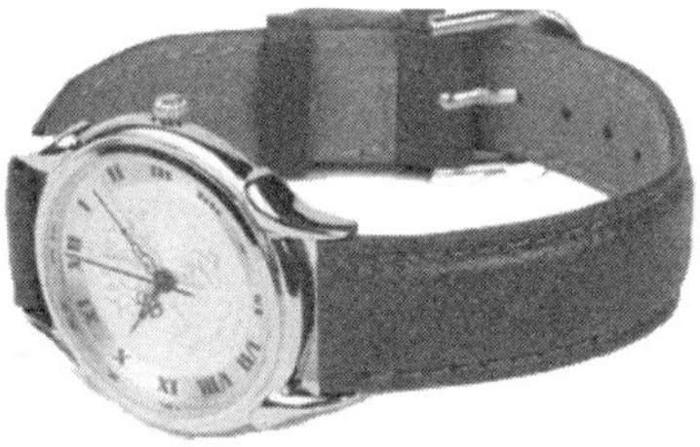

A  | B  | C

NAME ______________________

## LISTENING II

***(Track 22)* Listen to the question and three answers. What is the correct answer: A, B, or C?**

**3.** A. Yes, he does.
B. He needs red socks.
C. Too bad.

**4.** A. No, I'm sorry. We don't.
B. Hi. Yes. I need to return these shoes.
C. Well, here you go.

***(Track 23)* Listen to the conversation. Then listen to the question and three answers. What is the correct answer: A, B, or C?**

**5.** A. She doesn't have a receipt.
B. The zipper on the dress doesn't work.
C. The dress doesn't fit.

**6.** A. a medium shirt
B. a small shirt
C. a green T-shirt

NAME ____________________

# LIFE SKILLS I

***(Track 24)*** **Look at the pictures and listen. What is the correct answer: A, B, or C?**

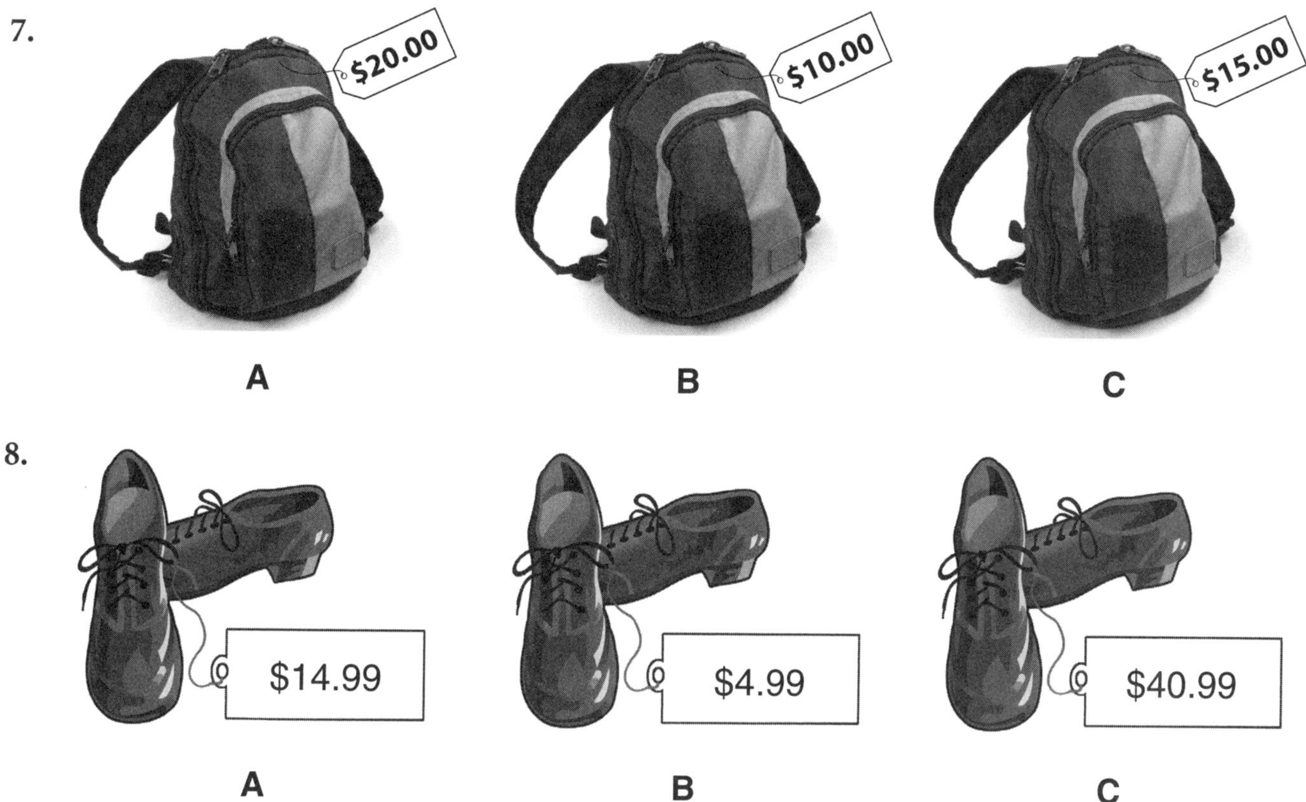

NAME ______________________

## GRAMMAR

### Complete each conversation. What is the correct answer: A, B, or C?

**9. A:** Your wallet is old.
**B:** Yes. I ______ a new wallet.

A. need
B. needs
C. has

**10. A:** Does Linda need blue shoes?
**B:** ______ doesn't.

A. Yes, she
B. No, she
C. No,

**11. A:** May I help you?
**B:** Yes. My wife ______ this watch. I need to return it.

A. don't want
B. don't like
C. doesn't like

**12. A:** Is this John's jacket?
**B:** No. He ______ a brown jacket.

A. has
B. want
C. need

**13. A:** Those jeans don't fit.
**B:** I know. I ______ a medium.

A. has
B. wants
C. need

**14. A:** You ______ a new jacket.
**B:** Yes, I do. The zipper on my jacket doesn't work.

A. don't need
B. doesn't need
C. don't

**15. A:** ______ this dress in size 4?
**B:** No, we don't.

A. You have
B. Do you have
C. Have

16. **A:** Do you have these T-shirts in blue? My children ______ yellow.
**B:** Yes, we do.

A. doesn't like
B. doesn't need
C. don't like

17. **A:** Do you want a backpack for your birthday?
**B:** OK! I ______ a backpack.

A. doesn't have
B. don't have
C. doesn't

18. **A:** Sej and Young Sun ______ those socks.
**B:** OK. How much are they?

A. need
B. has
C. wants

19. **A:** ______ need this jacket in a medium?
**B:** Yes, he does.

A. Does he
B. Does
C. He does

20. **A:** Do they want these large backpacks?
**B:** No, ______.

A. they have
B. he does
C. they don't

21. **A:** That dress ______ her.
**B:** I know. It's too big.

A. don't fit
B. doesn't fit
C. fit

22. **A:** Do Todd and Paul want red sweaters?
**B:** Yes, ______.

A. they do
B. they don't
C. we don't

23. **A:** Brenda ______ a new jacket.
**B:** How about this blue jacket?

A. want
B. wants
C. have

NAME ___________________________

## VOCABULARY

### Read. What is the correct answer: A, B, C, or D?

Mona

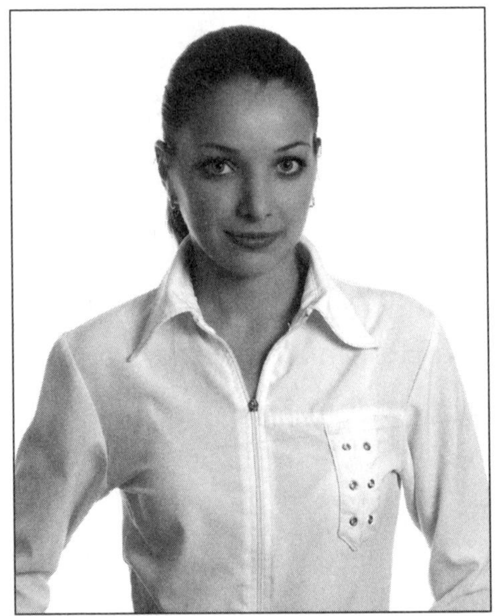

Ivana

**24.** What color is Mona's sweater?

A. blue
B. white
C. gray
D. black

**25.** What color is Ivana's shirt?

A. white
B. red
C. green
D. black

**Read. What is the correct answer: A, B, C, or D?**

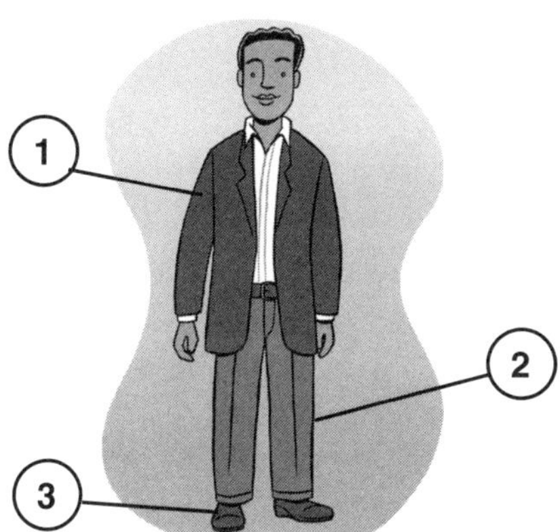


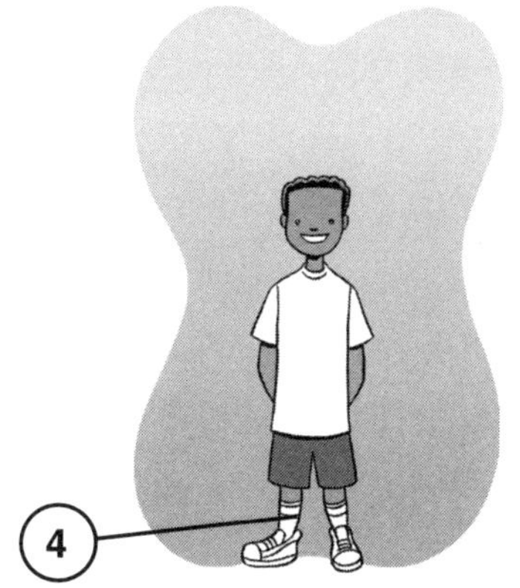


**26.** He has gray pants.

A. ①
B. ②
C. ③
D. ④

**27.** He has new socks.

A. ①
B. ②
C. ③
D. ④

NAME ____________________

# LIFE SKILLS II

## Read. What is the correct answer: A, B, C, or D?

Juan

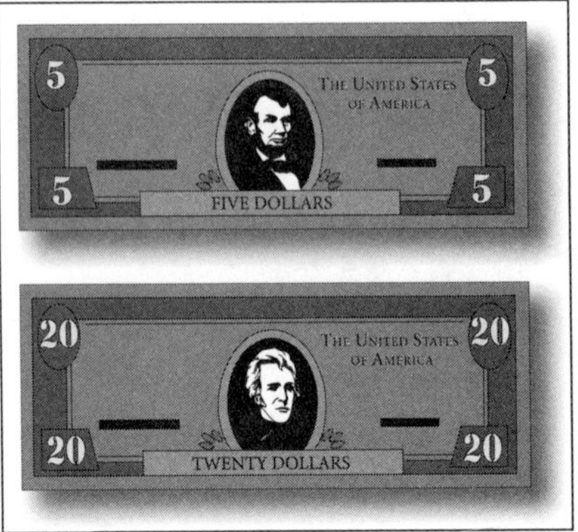


Ying

**28.** What coins does Juan have?

A. a dime and a penny

B. a nickel and a quarter

C. a penny and a quarter

D. a penny and a nickel

**29.** Count Ying's money. How much is it?

A. five dollars

B. fifteen dollars

C. twenty dollars

D. twenty-five dollars

NAME ____________________

**Read. What is the correct answer: A, B, C, or D?**

```
IMAGINE
Los Angeles, CA 90027
(213)555-0611

03-004-008                12:05 p.m.

WOMEN'S BLOUSES                12.99
WOMEN'S SHOES                  20.99
WOMEN'S JACKETS                34.99

SUBTOTAL                       68.97
TAX 8% ON 68.97                 5.52

TOTAL                          74.49

CASH AMOUNT PAID              100.00
CHANGE DUE                     25.51

Please keep receipt for returns.
Thank you for shopping at
IMAGINE.
```

**30.** How much are the shoes?

A. $12.99
B. $20.99
C. $34.99
D. $68.97

**31.** How much is the subtotal?

A. $100.00
B. $5.52
C. $74.49
D. $68.97

# READING

## Read. What is the correct answer: A, B, C, or D?

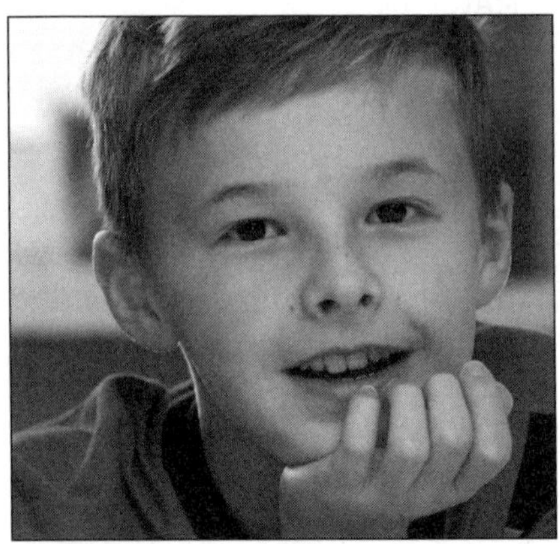

Tommy wants black sneakers, but he needs blue pants for school. Tommy and his mother go to the department store. The store has black sneakers, but they are $99.99! The store has blue pants. They are $15.99. Tommy's mother buys the pants for Tommy.

**32.** What does Tommy need?

A. black sneakers

B. white sneakers

C. blue pants

D. black pants

**33.** How much are the sneakers?

A. They are black.

B. They are $99.99.

C. They are brown.

D. They are $15.99.

NAME______________________________

# Unit 6 Test

## LISTENING I

***(Track 25)*** **Look at the pictures and listen. What is the correct answer: A, B, or C?**

1.

**A** **B** **C**

2.

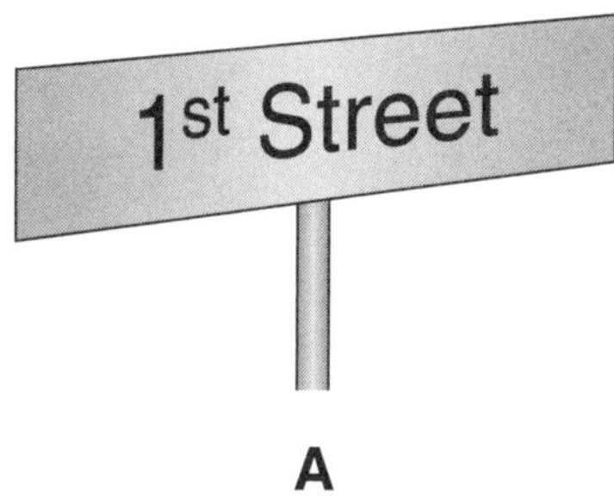


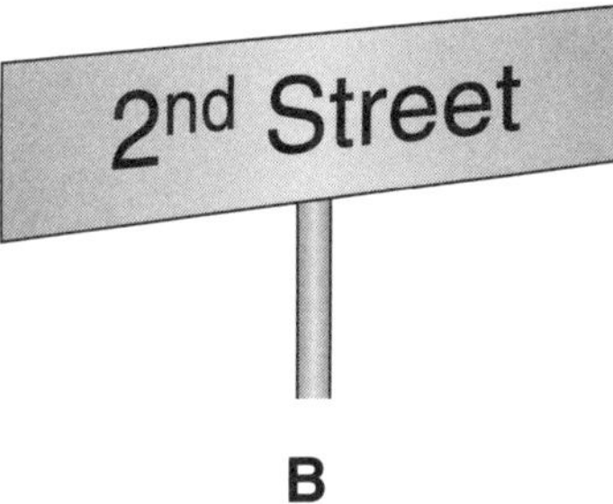

**A** **B** **C**

NAME ____________________

## LISTENING II

***(Track 26)* Listen to the question and three answers. What is the correct answer: A, B, or C?**

**3.** A. Oh, great. Is it furnished?
B. What about a dining room?
C. Yes, it's on the third floor.

**4.** A. Turn left on Sixth Avenue.
B. Excuse me.
C. Yes. There's a refrigerator.

***(Track 27)* Listen to the conversation. Then listen to the question and three answers. What is the correct answer: A, B, or C?**

**5.** A. It's sunny.
B. It's new.
C. There is no bathroom.

**6.** A. There's a coffee table, but no sofa.
B. There's a sofa and a coffee table.
C. There's a sofa, but no coffee table.

NAME ______________________________

## LIFE SKILLS I

***(Track 28)*** **Look at the pictures and listen. What is the correct answer: A, B, or C?**

7.

| 242 N. Main St.<br>Apartment C | 442 N. Banes St.<br>Apartment 13 | 222 N. Main St.<br>Apartment 3 |
|---|---|---|
| **A** | **B** | **C** |

NAME________________________________________

# GRAMMAR

## Complete each conversation. What is the correct answer: A, B, or C?

**8. A:** Tell us about your apartment!
**B:** ______ one bedroom.

A. There's
B. There are
C. There's no

**9. A:** What's in the downstairs bedroom?
**B:** Well, ______ bed!

A. it's
B. there's a
C. there are

**10. A:** Tell me about your bathroom.
**B:** Well, ______ a bathtub.

A. there are
B. is there
C. there's

**11. A:** Are there sofas in the living room?
**B:** Yes, ______.

A. there are
B. there aren't
C. there is

**12. A:** ______ a microwave?
**B:** Yes, there is.

A. Are there
B. Is there
C. There are

**13. A:** Are there chairs in the kitchen?
**B:** No, ______.

A. there aren't
B. there is
C. there's

**14. A:** Where's the appliance store?
**B:** It's ______ 111 Vermont Street.

A. to
B. in
C. at

15. **A:** How do I get to the store ______ here?
**B:** Go to Third Street and turn left. It's across from the apartment building.

A. to
B. from
C. on

16. **A:** Where's her new apartment?
**B:** It's ______ Los Angeles.

A. from
B. in
C. at

17. **A:** ______ closets in your bedroom?
**B:** Yes, there are.

A. Is there
B. Are there
C. There aren't

18. **A:** How do I get to the school from here?
**B:** Go ______ Smith Street and turn left.

A. in
B. from
C. to

19. **A:** Where is your apartment?
**B:** It's ______ the corner of First and Crown Valley Avenue.

A. from
B. to
C. on

20. **A:** What's in the kitchen of your new apartment?
**B:** ______ a refrigerator.

A. There are
B. There's
C. There aren't

21. **A:** There's a table and sofa in the living room, but ______ chairs.
**B:** Oh.

A. there are no
B. there is no
C. there's no

22. **A:** Is there a closet in the bedroom?
**B:** No, ______.

A. there isn't
B. there is
C. there aren't

# VOCABULARY

## Read. What is the correct answer: A, B, C, or D?

**23.** What is in the dining room?

A. a bed and a lamp
B. a table and chairs
C. a sofa and a table
D. a toilet and a bathtub

**24.** What is in the kitchen?

A. a refrigerator and a stove
B. a sink and a bathtub
C. a lamp and a sofa
D. a table and chairs

**25.** Where is the dresser?

A. in the dining room
B. in the kitchen
C. in the bathroom
D. in the bedroom

**26.** Where is the shower?

A. in the kitchen
B. in the bedroom
C. in the bathroom
D. in the laundry room

# LIFE SKILLS II

## Read. What is the correct answer: A, B, C, or D?

4 BR/2 BA Apt. in New Bldg.
$1,400 Utils. Incl.
35 Cole Ave.
Citywide Rentals
(213) 555-4488

①

3 BR/2 BA House $1,700
Lndry, A/C
400 Franklin Ave.
(818) 444-0554

②

1 BR/1 BA Apt., $500
Utils. incl.
4100 Loz Feliz Blvd.
(323) 909-4432

③

2 BR/2 BA House $1,900
Lg Kit, Pkg
2445 Fairview St.
(563) 444-9876

④

**27.** Which apartment or house has four bedrooms?

A. ①
B. ②
C. ③
D. ④

**28.** Which apartment or house has air conditioning?

A. ①
B. ②
C. ③
D. ④

**29.** Which apartments or houses have utilities included in the rent?

A. ① and ②
B. ③ and ④
C. ① and ③
D. ② and ④

## Read. What is the correct answer: A, B, C, or D?

Max Chow
4202 Steinway Blvd.
Astoria, NY 11102

Pedro Martinez
1500 Azalea St., Apt. 5C
Mountain View, CA 94202



**30.** Who is the letter to?

A. Max Chow

B. Astoria, NY

C. Pedro Martinez

D. Mountain View, CA

**31.** Where does Pedro Martinez live?

A. on Steinway Boulevard

B. in the state of New York

C. at 5C Azalea Street

D. in the city of Mountain View

# READING

## Read. What is the correct answer: A, B, C, or D?

Antonio and Marta live in Greenville. They need a new apartment with two bedrooms. There are two apartments on Eleventh Street. The first apartment is cheap. There is no air conditioning, but there are sunny bedrooms. The second apartment is expensive. There's a dining room. Antonio and Marta get the cheap apartment. They love it!

**32.** What do Antonio and Marta need?

A. sunny bedrooms
B. a two-bedroom apartment
C. an expensive apartment
D. air conditioning

**33.** What does the cheap apartment have?

A. air conditioning
B. two bathrooms
C. no air conditioning
D. a dining room

NAME ____________________

# Unit 7 Test

## LISTENING I

**(Track 29) Look at the pictures and listen. What is the correct answer: A, B, or C?**

1.

A

B

C

2.

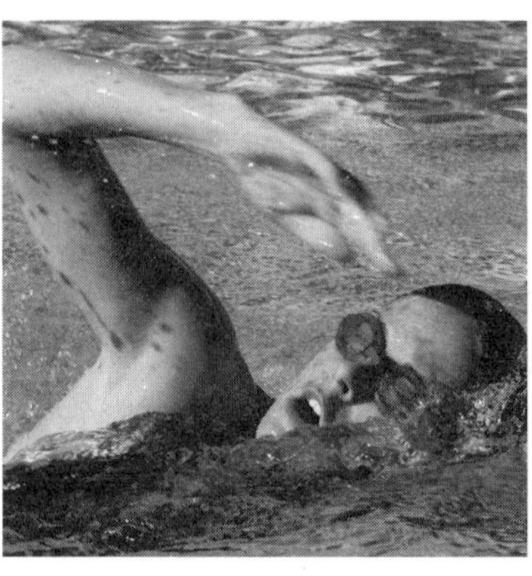

A

B

C

NAME ____________________

# LISTENING II

***(Track 30)* Listen to the question and three answers. What is the correct answer: A, B, or C?**

**3.** A. Me, too.
B. At 8:00.
C. I always do the laundry.

**4.** A. Are you free tomorrow?
B. That's a good idea.
C. At 5:00.

***(Track 31)* Listen to the conversation. Then listen to the question and three answers. What is the correct answer: A, B, or C?**

**5.** A. Yes, he is.
B. No, he isn't. He visits his family on Sundays.
C. No, he isn't. He goes to movies on Sundays.

**6.** A. every day
B. every weekend
C. never

# GRAMMAR

## Complete each conversation. What is the correct answer: A, B, or C?

7. **A:** ______ does class start?
   **B:** At 7:30.
   A. What
   B. When
   C. How often

8. **A:** When does Bao play soccer?
   **B:** ______ Saturdays at 10:00 A.M.
   A. At
   B. On
   C. From

9. **A:** I clean my house at night after work.
   **B:** I ______ clean the house at night. I always clean it in the morning.
   A. always
   B. never
   C. usually

10. **A:** Tina, what time do you have dinner ______ Saturdays?
    **B:** I eat at 6:00 P.M.
    A. on
    B. in
    C. to

11. **A:** What time do they have breakfast?
    **B:** ______ 7:00 to 7:45 A.M.
    A. In
    B. On
    C. From

12. **A:** What time do the boys work?
    **B:** They work from 4:00 ______ 6:00 P.M.
    A. in
    B. to
    C. at

13. **A:** ______ do you visit your friends?
    **B:** Twice a week.
    A. What time
    B. Where
    C. How often

14. **A:** I don't watch TV from Monday to Friday. But I ______ watch football on Sunday afternoons!
**B:** Wow! *Every* Sunday?

A. never
B. sometimes
C. always

15. **A:** ______ does Mrs. Cordova cook dinner for her family?
**B:** Oh, three times a week.

A. What
B. How often
C. What time

16. **A:** How often does he work at the restaurant?
**B:** ______ a week.

A. Once
B. Two
C. One

17. **A:** Danuta, what time do you play soccer on Saturday morning?
**B:** I always play soccer ______ 8:00 A.M.

A. on
B. at
C. in

18. **A:** ______ does your son go food shopping?
**B:** Every week.

A. What time
B. What
C. How often

19. **A:** ______ do they get home from school?
**B:** At 3:30.

A. How often
B. What
C. What time

NAME______________________________

**Look at Diego's weekly schedule. Then complete each conversation. What is the correct answer: A, B, or C?**

| | MONDAY | TUESDAY | WEDNESDAY | THURSDAY | FRIDAY |
|---|---|---|---|---|---|
| **morning** | English class | English class | English class | | |
| **afternoon** | | | | English class | |
| **night** | work | work | watch TV | watch TV | watch TV |

**20. A:** Does Diego work at night?
**B:** Yes, he does. He ______ works at night.

A. sometimes
B. never
C. always

**21. A:** How often does Diego go to English class?
**B:** He ______ goes to English class in the morning, but sometimes he goes in the afternoon.

A. usually
B. never
C. always

NAME ______________________________

# VOCABULARY

**Read. What is the correct answer: A, B, C, or D?**

**Polly**

**Cecilia and Karen**

**22.** What does Polly do at 8:00 P.M.?

A. She eats breakfast.

B. She gets home.

C. She watches TV.

D. She washes the dishes.

**23.** What do Cecilia and Karen do every Saturday?

A. They get up.

B. They go to work.

C. They cook dinner.

D. They eat dinner at a restaurant.

## Read. What is the correct answer: A, B, C, or D?

①

②

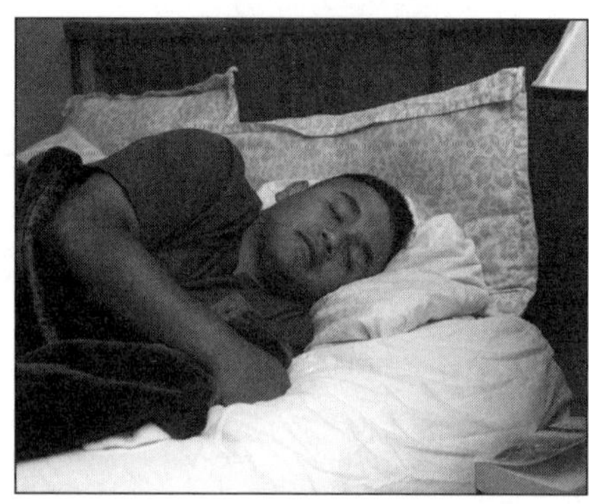

③

④

**24.** Leo takes a shower at 7:30 A.M.

A. ①
B. ②
C. ③
D. ④

**25.** Leo exercises every day.

A. ①
B. ②
C. ③
D. ④

# LIFE SKILLS

## Read. What is the correct answer: A, B, C, or D?

**Metro Department Store Work Schedule**
Week: April 10–April 17

| Name | Department | Days | Hours |
|---|---|---|---|
| Brady, Tom | shoes | Wed.–Sat. | 9:00–1:00 |
| Gomez, Maria | dresses | Sun., Mon., Tues., Thurs. | 12:00–8:30 |
| Nam, Lin | ladies' coats | Mon.–Fri. | 1:00–5:00 |
| Perez, Ricardo | office | Sat. & Sun. | 8:00–4:00 |

**26.** When does Lin Nam work?
- A. Sunday to Thursday, from 9:00–1:00
- B. Monday to Thursday, from 10:00–3:00
- C. Saturday and Sunday, from 8:00–4:00
- D. Monday to Friday, from 1:00–5:00

**27.** What time does Tom Brady start work?
- A. 9:00
- B. 12:00
- C. 1:00
- D. 8:00

**28.** How often does Ricardo Perez work?
- A. every day
- B. once a week
- C. twice a week
- D. three times a week

**Read. What is the correct answer: A, B, C, or D?**

| TIME SHEET | | | |
|---|---|---|---|
| EMPLOYEE NAME<br>*Cha* (Last) *Chan-Sook* (First) | | | EMPLOYEE I.D. #<br>*988-066-04133* |
| Week ending *8/15* | | | |
| | TIME IN | TIME OUT | HOURS |
| Sun. | *off* | | |
| Mon. | *8:00 A.M.* | *5:00 P.M.* | *9* |
| Tues. | *off* | | |
| Wed. | *8:00 A.M.* | *5:00 P.M.* | *9* |
| Thurs. | *off* | | |
| Fri. | *off* | | |
| Sat. | *off* | | |
| Employee Signature *Chan-Sook Cha* | | | TOTAL HOURS<br>*18* |

**29.** When does Chan-Sook work?

A. Monday, from 8:00 A.M. to 6:00 P.M.

B. Monday and Tuesday, from 8:00 A.M. to 5:00 P.M.

C. Monday and Wednesday, from 8:00 A.M. to 5:00 P.M.

D. Tuesday and Thursday, from 8:00 A.M. to 5:00 P.M.

**30.** When is Chan-Sook off?

A. Monday and Wednesday

B. Monday and Tuesday

C. Wednesday, Thursday, Friday, Saturday, and Sunday

D. Tuesday, Thursday, Friday, Saturday, and Sunday

**31.** How many hours does Chan-Sook work every week?

A. 0

B. 5

C. 9

D. 18

NAME ______________________________

# READING

## Read. What is the correct answer: A, B, C, or D?

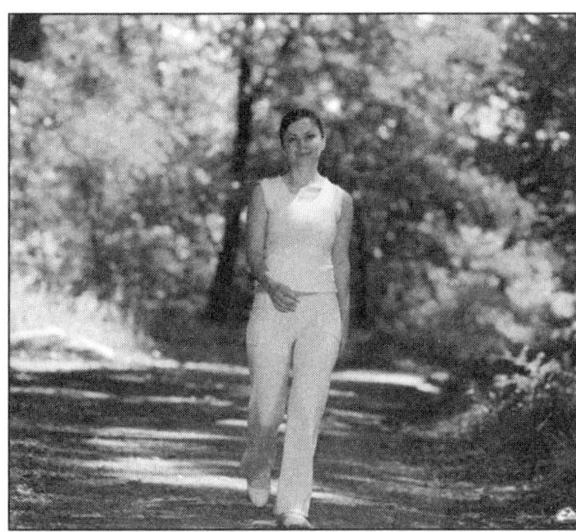

Cali is a waitress. She works Monday to Friday, from 8:00 A.M. to 5:00 P.M. On Saturdays and Sundays, she always gets up late. Then she takes a long walk. Cali is stressed at her job during the week. So, on weekends she relaxes.

**32.** What time does Cali start work?

A. 5:00 P.M.
B. 8:00 A.M.
C. Monday to Friday
D. every day

**33.** What does she usually do on weekends?

A. She works at a restaurant.
B. She is stressed.
C. She gets up early.
D. She relaxes.

NAME____________________

# Unit 8 Test

## LISTENING I

***(Track 32)*** **Look at the pictures and listen. What is the correct answer: A, B, or C?**

1.

**A**  **B** 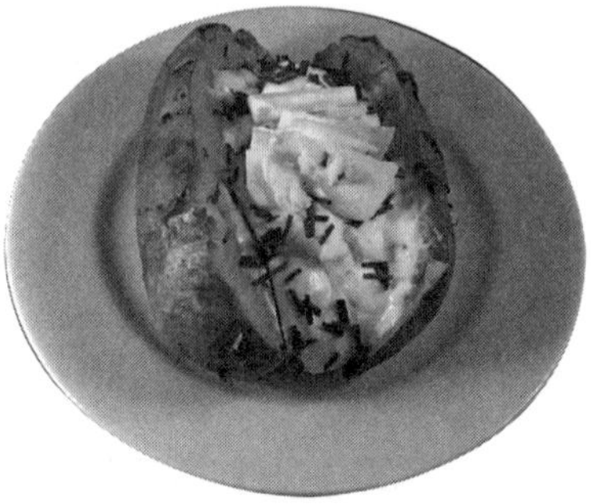 **C**

2.

**A**  **B**  **C**

# LISTENING II

***(Track 33)* Listen to the question and three answers. What is the correct answer: A, B, or C?**

**3.** A. Yes, I'd like a green salad and a cup of coffee.
B. Large, please.
C. Coffee is good.

**4.** A. Two pounds.
B. What about you?
C. OK. How much salmon do we need?

***(Track 34)* Listen to the conversation. Then listen to the question and three answers. What is the correct answer: A, B, or C?**

**5.** A. The man likes soup.
B. The man doesn't like cucumbers.
C. The man doesn't like salad.

**6.** A. pizza
B. iced tea
C. cheese

NAME ____________________

## LIFE SKILLS I

***(Track 35)* Look at the pictures and listen. What is the correct answer: A, B, or C?**

7.

8.

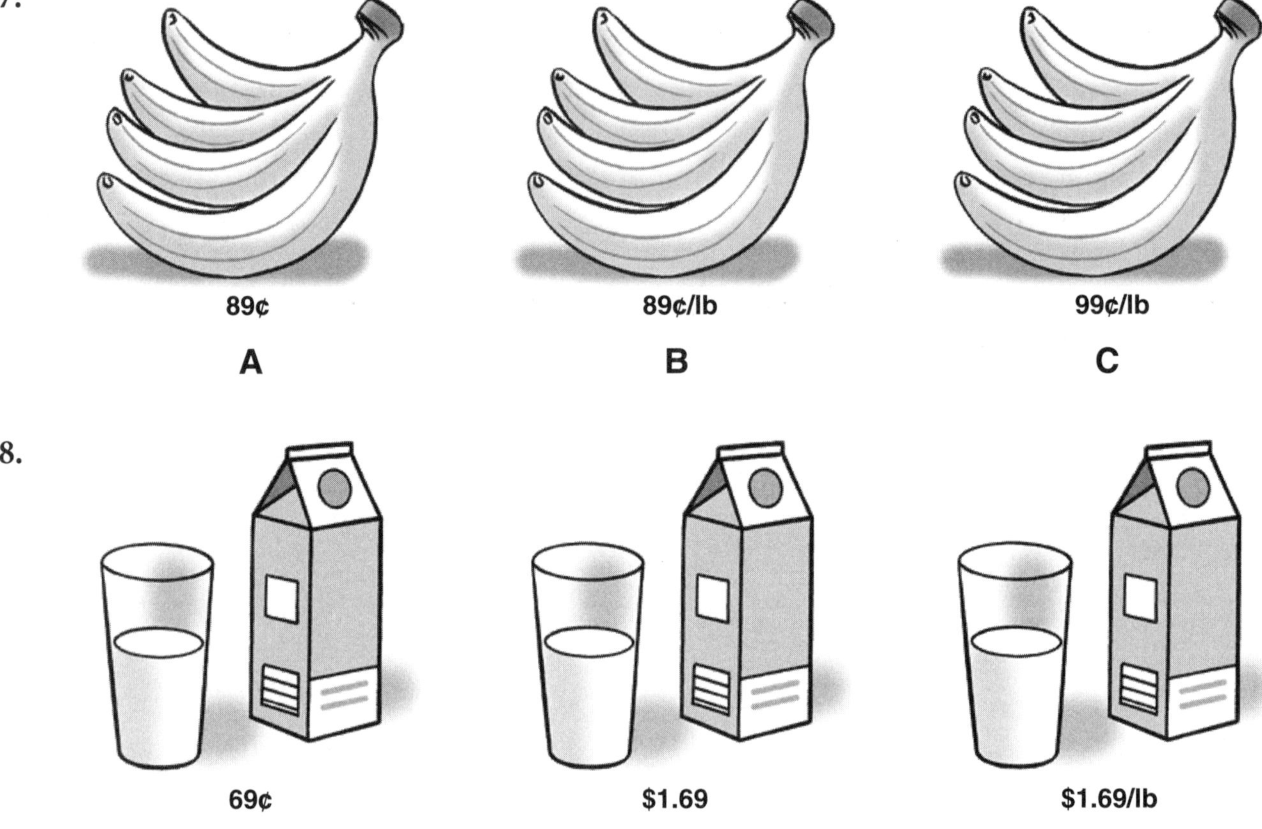

NAME ______________________________

# GRAMMAR

**Complete each conversation. What is the correct answer: A, B, or C?**

**9. A:** I love ______!
**B:** I know. It's good for you.

A. onion
B. rice
C. apple

**10. A:** Do you want a ______?
**B:** Thanks, but I don't like them.

A. banana
B. milk
C. cheese

**11. A:** ______ bread is there?
**B:** A lot. We don't need more.

A. How many
B. How much
C. What

**12. A:** ______ are good for you.
**B:** Really?

A. Beef
B. Fish
C. Oranges

**13. A:** Would you like ______?
**B:** Beans, please.

A. beans
B. milk or water
C. beans or rice

**14. A:** Do you want ______?
**B:** I want cereal, please.

A. cereal
B. yogurt or cereal
C. or cereal

**15. A:** ______ potatoes do we have?
**B:** Only two.

A. How many
B. What
C. How much

16. **A:** Would you like ______?
**B:** Shrimp, please!

A. shrimp or roast beef
B. salad or yogurt
C. cucumbers or olives

17. **A:** ______ butter is there?
**B:** Not much. We need more.

A. How many
B. When
C. How much

18. **A:** How many onions do you have?
**B:** ______. And they're small. We need more.

A. Not many
B. Not much
C. A lot

19. **A:** Do you have any ______?
**B:** Yes, of course. We eat it with rice twice a week.

A. chicken
B. eggs
C. potatoes

20. **A:** I love ______. I eat them for lunch every day.
**B:** Me, too!

A. cheese
B. apples
C. butter

21. **A:** Would you like coffee or milk?
**B:** ______, please.

A. An iced tea
B. Orange juice
C. Coffee

22. **A:** How many tomatoes do we have?
**B:** ______. And they are big.

A. Not much
B. A lot
C. Only one

23. **A:** I like ______ for breakfast. What about you?
**B:** I don't like them. I like cereal.

A. eggs
B. yogurt
C. bread

NAME ______________________

# VOCABULARY

## Read. What is the correct answer: A, B, C, or D?

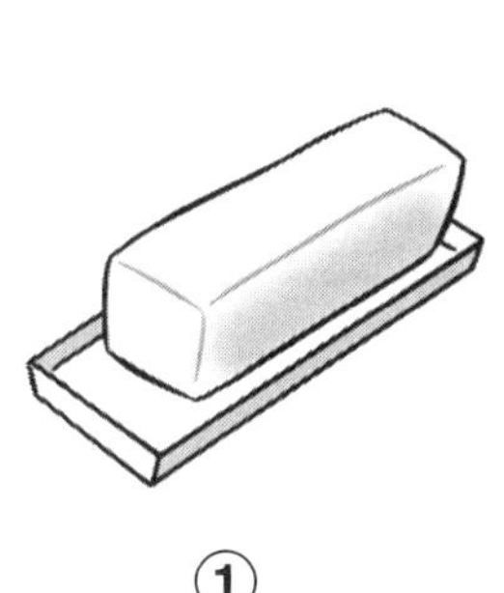
①

②

③

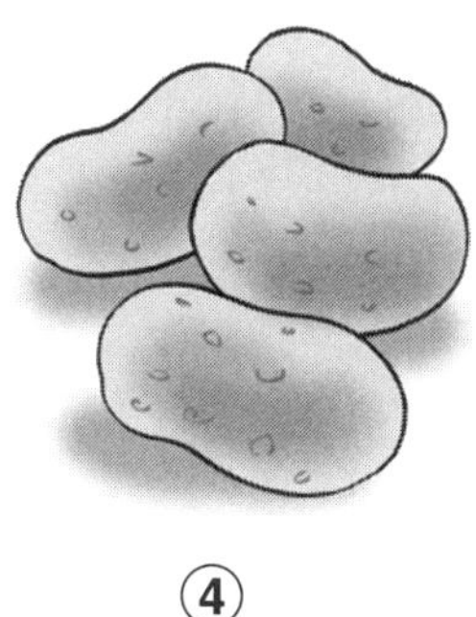
④

**24.** I don't really like oranges.

A. ①
B. ②
C. ③
D. ④

**25.** I love onions.

A. ①
B. ②
C. ③
D. ④

NAME ____________________

**Read. What is the correct answer: A, B, C, or D?**

①

②

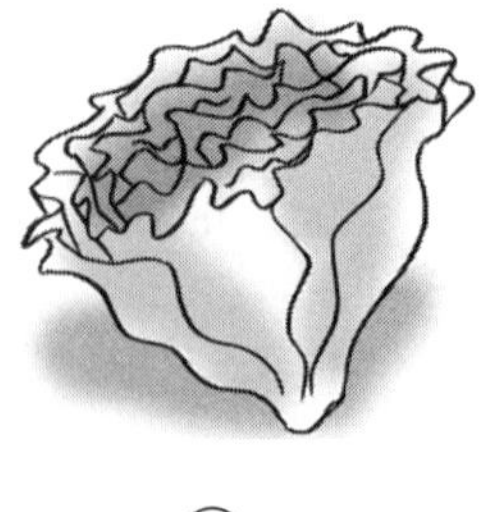

③

④

**26.** What kind of food is ①?

A. grain

B. fruit

C. oil

D. dairy

**27.** Which foods are in the meat and beans food group?

A. ① and ②

B. ② and ③

C. ② and ④

D. ③ and ④

NAME ______________________________

## LIFE SKILLS II

### Read. What is the correct answer: A, B, C, or D?

**Yogurt Nutrition Facts**

Serving Size: 8 oz.

Servings per Container: 1

| | |
|---|---|
| Calories | 230 |
| Total fat | 2 g |
| Sodium | 150 mg |
| Sugar | 41 g |

**28.** How many calories are in one serving of yogurt?

A. 8 oz.

B. 1

C. 230

D. 150 mg

**29.** How much sugar is in one serving of yogurt?

A. 8 oz.

B. 2 g

C. 150 mg

D. 41 g

NAME ______________________________

**Read. What is the correct answer: A, B, C, or D?**

| TIPS TO STAY HEALTHY | | |
|---|---|---|
| Don't eat a lot of fat. | Don't eat a lot of sodium. | Don't eat a lot of sugar. |

*Eat the right amount of calories.*

**30.** Which food is healthy?

A. salad

B. pie

C. ice cream

D. French fries

**31.** Which food has a lot of sodium?

A. salad

B. pie

C. ice cream

D. French fries

NAME ______________________

# READING

## Read. What is the correct answer: A, B, C, or D?

Cameron usually eats lunch at the food court. Cameron loves hamburgers. He eats one or two hamburgers every day. He drinks a large soda with the hamburgers. Hamburgers have a lot of sodium and fat. So Cameron has healthy food for dinner. He eats fish or chicken, and he drinks milk.

**32.** How many hamburgers does Cameron eat every day?

A. a lot

B. one or two

C. three

D. many large hamburgers

**33.** What does Cameron drink every day?

A. a small soda for lunch

B. milk for lunch

C. a large soda for dinner

D. soda and milk

NAME ______________________________

# Unit 9 Test

## LISTENING I

*(Track 36)* **Look at the pictures and listen. What is the correct answer: A, B, or C?**

1.

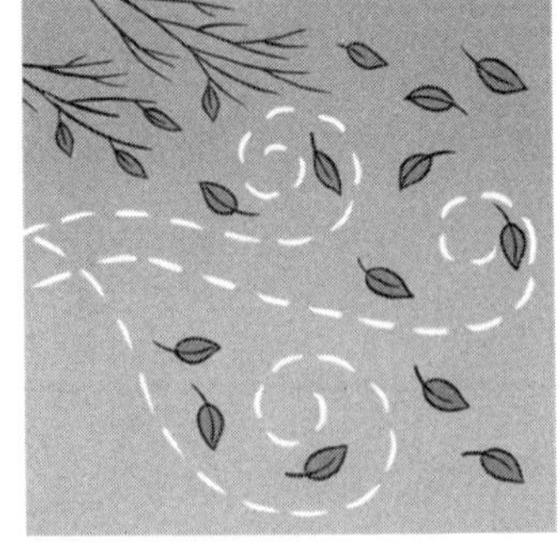

A

B

C

2.

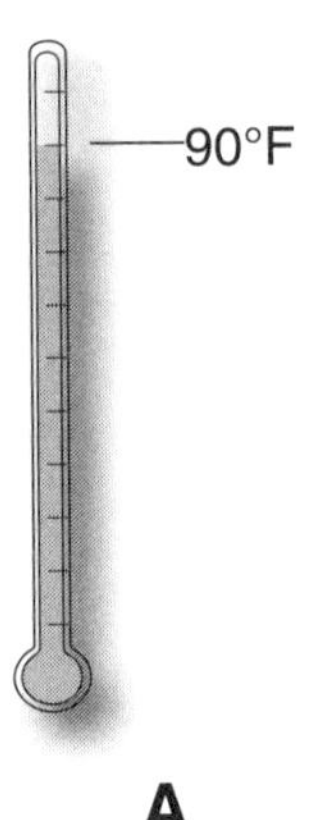


A

50°F

B

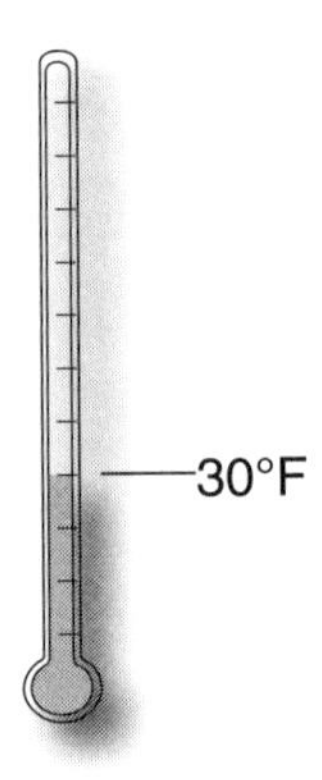


C

# LISTENING II

***(Track 37)* Listen to the question and three answers. What is the correct answer: A, B, or C?**

**3.** A. Yes. Why?
B. I'm in Denver.
C. It's cold and rainy.

**4.** A. I'm shopping.
B. No, I'm not.
C. That's OK. I have sunblock.

***(Track 38)* Listen to the conversation. Then listen to the question and three answers. What is the correct answer: A, B, or C?**

**5.** A. She's reading.
B. She's watching TV.
C. She's checking e-mail.

**6.** A. a hurricane
B. a thunderstorm
C. a snowstorm

NAME ______________________________

## GRAMMAR

### Complete each conversation. What is the correct answer: A, B, or C?

7. **A:** What are you doing?
   **B:** ______ talking to my friend.
   A. She
   B. He's
   C. I'm

8. **A:** Are you watching TV?
   **B:** No, ______.
   A. we're not
   B. she's not
   C. he's not

9. **A:** I'm hungry. Let's eat.
   **B:** OK. There's a ______ restaurant on Fourth Street.
   A. really
   B. very
   C. very good

10. **A:** Is Carolina wearing a new shirt?
    **B:** No, ______.
    A. she is
    B. they aren't
    C. she isn't

11. **A:** It's sunny today.
    **B:** No, it isn't. It ______.
    A. raining
    B. is raining
    C. is it raining

12. **A:** How is the weather?
    **B:** It's ______.
    A. very
    B. really hot
    C. pretty

13. **A:** It's ______ tonight!
    **B:** I know. A hurricane is coming!
    A. very windy
    B. not windy
    C. really

**14. A:** Sundar is watching TV.
**B:** No, he isn't. He's ______.

A. talk
B. working
C. is working

**15. A:** Is it foggy there?
**B:** Yes, it's ______ foggy.

A. not
B. pretty
C. rainy

**16. A:** Is Ana working?
**B:** No, she isn't. She ______ in the park with her sister.

A. are walking
B. walking
C. is walking

**17. A:** ______ talking on the phone?
**B:** No, he's not.

A. Are your brothers
B. Your brother is
C. Is your brother

**18. A:** ______ Min and Peichi shopping?
**B:** No, they aren't.

A. Is
B. Are
C. They are

**19. A:** Are you tired?
**B:** Yes. I'm ______.

A. pretty
B. not
C. very tired

**20. A:** Is Mom wearing a skirt?
**B:** Yes, she ______.

A. isn't
B. is
C. are

**21. A:** Are you reading a book?
**B:** No, ______ not.

A. I'm
B. she's
C. they're

NAME ______________________

## VOCABULARY

### Read. What is the correct answer: A, B, C, or D?

①

②

③

④

**22.** It's cloudy today.

A. ①

B. ②

C. ③

D. ④

**23.** It's snowy in winter.

A. ①

B. ②

C. ③

D. ④

NAME___

**Read. What is the correct answer: A, B, C, or D?**

①

②

③

④

**24.** What's the weather like in picture ①?

A. cool and cloudy

B. cold and snowy

C. warm and rainy

D. hot and sunny

**25.** What's the weather like in picture ④?

A. cool and cloudy

B. cold and snowy

C. warm and rainy

D. hot and sunny

## LIFE SKILLS

### Read. What is the correct answer: A, B, C, or D?

①

②

③

④

**26.** Don't go swimming in a thunderstorm.

A. ①
B. ②
C. ③
D. ④

**27.** Go downstairs in a tornado.

A. ①
B. ②
C. ③
D. ④

**Read. What is the correct answer: A, B, C, or D?**

Emergency Family Plan

Places to meet

1. Outside our apartment building
2. Main post office: 2209 7th Street

Emergency phone numbers

Carla
Work (510) 555-8317
Cell (510) 555-1194

Luis
Work (510) 555-7835
Cell (510) 555-7834

Maria
School (510) 555-4965

Uncle Alex (312) 555-0552

**28.** Where is the family meeting in an emergency?

A. at school

B. at the post office

C. at the mall

D. at the park

**29.** Which emergency phone number is long distance?

A. Carla's number

B. Luis's number

C. Maria's number

D. Uncle Alex's number

## Read. What is the correct answer: A, B, C, or D?

①

②

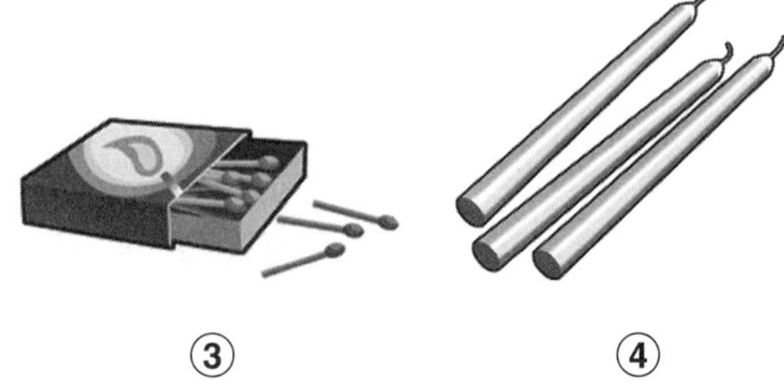

③ ④

**30.** You need batteries in an emergency.

A. ①

B. ②

C. ③

D. ④

**31.** You need matches and candles in an emergency.

A. ① and ②

B. ② and ③

C. ③ and ④

D. ① and ④

# READING

## Read. What is the correct answer: A, B, C, or D?

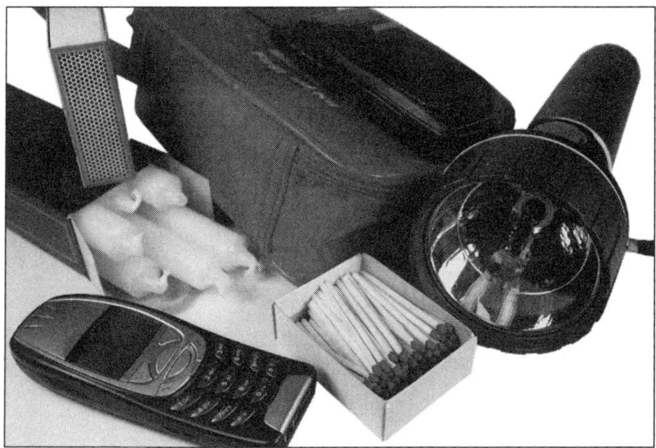

David is from Chicago. It's very cold in Chicago in winter. Now he is living in California. It's sunny and hot in California. But there are earthquakes. David has a bag of things for an emergency. He has a first aid kit, a radio, a flashlight, candles, and matches in the bag. He has a cell phone, too.

**32.** What's the weather like in California?
- A. It's sunny and hot.
- B. It's sunny and cold.
- C. It's very cold.
- D. There aren't earthquakes.

**33.** What does David have for an emergency?
- A. an earthquake
- B. a first aid kit and batteries
- C. a flashlight, candles, and matches
- D. a cell phone and water

NAME ____________________

# Unit 10 Test

## LISTENING I

***(Track 39)*** **Look at the pictures and listen. What is the correct answer: A, B, or C?**

1.

**A** **B** **C**

2.

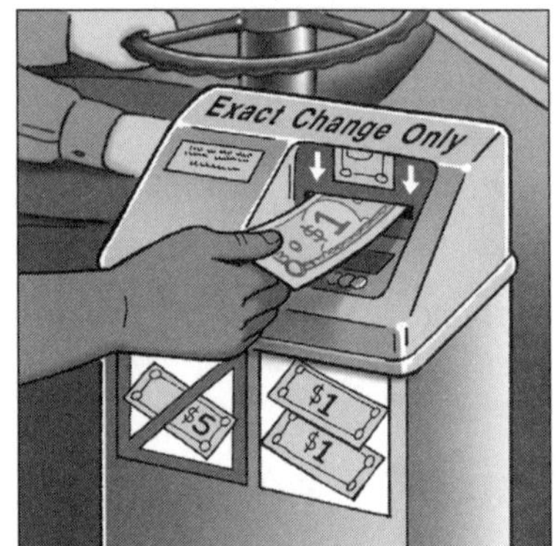

**A** **B** **C**

NAME ____________________

## LISTENING II

***(Track 40)* Listen to the question and three answers. What is the correct answer: A, B, or C?**

**3.** A. Can you help me?
B. Sure.
C. One dollar.

**4.** A. At Greenville Shopping Mall.
B. I'm going to a yard sale.
C. Sounds great.

***(Track 41)* Listen to the conversation. Then listen to the question and three answers. What is the correct answer: A, B, or C?**

**5.** A. He's going to a concert.
B. He's going to a yard sale.
C. He's going to a baseball game.

**6.** A. To the community college.
B. To the courthouse.
C. To a coffee shop.

NAME_______________________________________________

## GRAMMAR

### Complete each conversation. What is the correct answer: A, B, or C?

**7. A:** Where's Java Joe Coffee Shop?
**B:** It's ______ the corner from the shopping center.

A. between
B. down
C. around

**8. A:** ______ do your grandparents get on the bus?
**B:** Near their house.

A. What
B. How much
C. Where

**9. A:** Is the ATM down the street?
**B:** No, it's ______ the library.

A. on
B. near
C. down

**10. A:** ______ does bread cost at the supermarket?
**B:** It's $1.75.

A. How much
B. How
C. Where

**11. A:** Where's the park?
**B:** It's ______ the street from the courthouse.

A. around
B. between
C. down

**12. A:** ______ do I buy tissues?
**B:** At the drugstore.

A. Where
B. How
C. How much

**13. A:** Who ______ to the concert with you?
**B:** My sister.

A. going
B. is going
C. are going

**14. A:** Excuse me. Where's the bank?
**B:** It's ______ the bus station and the hair salon.

A. between
B. to
C. down

**15. A:** I'm taking the bus to the beach.
**B:** ______ going with you?

A. Who
B. Who is
C. How is

**16. A:** ______ is a train ticket to San Diego?
**B:** It's $21.25.

A. How much
B. Where
C. How

**17. A:** ______ do they shop for food?
**B:** At the supermarket on Sixth Avenue.

A. How
B. Where
C. How much

**18. A:** What ______ tomorrow?
**B:** They're working tomorrow.

A. they doing
B. they are doing
C. are they doing

**19. A:** Who ______ to the concert tomorrow?
**B:** I'm driving.

A. is driving
B. 're driving
C. are driving

**20. A:** How do I get to Maxwell's Department Store?
**B:** It's ______ the corner of Pine and Rose Streets.

A. around
B. down
C. on

**21. A:** How is she getting to the mall tomorrow?
**B:** She ______ the bus.

A. take
B. 's taking
C. are taking

NAME ______________________

## VOCABULARY

### Read. What is the correct answer: A, B, C, or D?

①

②

③

④

**22.** How do you get to the fire station?

A. ①
B. ②
C. ③
D. ④

**23.** Is there a supermarket around here?

A. ①
B. ②
C. ③
D. ④

NAME ____________________

## Read. What is the correct answer: A, B, C, or D?

①

②

③

④

**24.** I'm looking for the library.

A. ①
B. ②
C. ③
D. ④

**25.** The bus stop is on Sixth Avenue.

A. ①
B. ②
C. ③
D. ④

NAME ______________________________

## LIFE SKILLS

### Read. What is the correct answer: A, B, C, or D?

①

②

③

④

**26.** Susana and Pedro take the train to work.

A. ①
B. ②
C. ③
D. ④

**27.** Al rides his bike to work.

A. ①
B. ②
C. ③
D. ④

NAME ______________________

**Read. What is the correct answer: A, B, C, or D?**

**28.** What is the meaning of the sign?

A. Two-way traffic. Drive on the right.

B. Drive slowly. People often cross the street here.

C. Be ready to stop for trains.

D. Don't drive here.

NAME ____________________

## Read. What is the correct answer: A, B, C, or D?

| RICHVILLE BUS SCHEDULES | | | | | | | |
|---|---|---|---|---|---|---|---|
| **BUS 14** | | **BUS 24** | | **BUS 34** | | **BUS 54** | |
| 1st St. | 7:46 | 5th St. | 7:56 | 10th St. | 7:58 | 14th St. | 8:11 |
| 3rd Ave. | 7:55 | 10th Ave. | 8:04 | 16th Ave. | 8:06 | 20th St. | 8:15 |
| Beach Blvd. | 8:11 | Gold Ave. | 8:12 | 21st Ave. | 8:15 | 24th St. | 8:18 |

**29.** Which bus leaves 10th Avenue at 8:04?

A. Bus 14
B. Bus 24
C. Bus 34
D. Bus 54

**30.** What time does Bus 34 leave 21st Avenue?

A. 7:46
B. 7:58
C. 8:06
D. 8:15

**31.** Which bus goes to 24th Street?

A. Bus 14
B. Bus 24
C. Bus 34
D. Bus 54

# READING

## Read. What is the correct answer: A, B, C, or D?

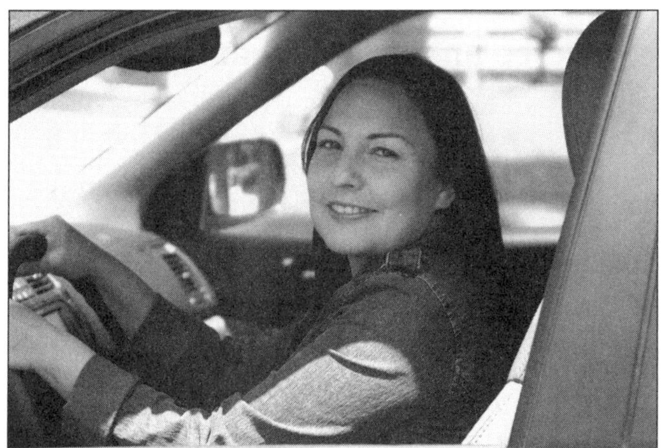

Jenny is very busy. Tomorrow, she is driving her car to work. At lunch, she is shopping at a department store. Then at 6:00 P.M. she is going to a restaurant with her friend Brad. Then they are walking to a free concert in the park. The park is around the corner from Jenny's apartment.

**32.** How is Jenny getting to work?

A. She is driving her car.

B. She is walking.

C. She is riding a bike.

D. She is taking the bus.

**33.** Where is Jenny going tomorrow night?

A. to work

B. to a department store

C. to Brad's apartment

D. to the park

NAME ____________________

# Unit 11 Test

## LISTENING I

***(Track 42)*** **Look at the pictures and listen. What is the correct answer: A, B, or C?**

1.

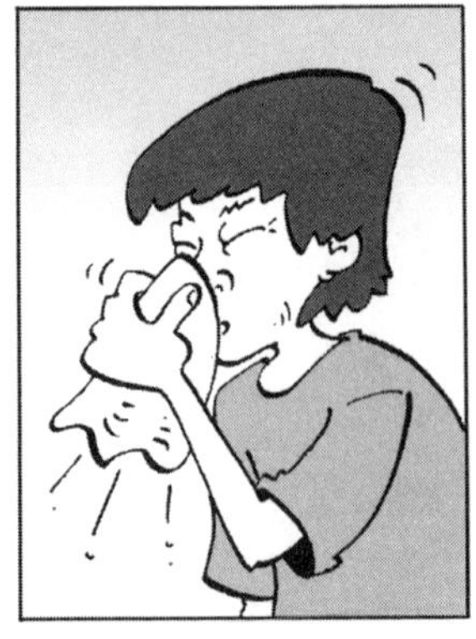

**A**

**B**

**C**

2.

**A**

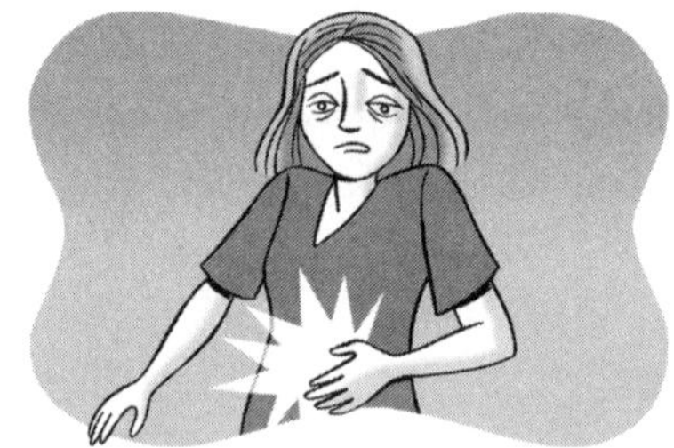

**B**

**C**

NAME ____________________

## LISTENING II

**(*Track 43*) Listen to the question and three answers. What is the correct answer: A, B, or C?**

**3.** A. Oh, too bad. How is he today?
B. I wasn't here yesterday.
C. A lot better, thanks.

**4.** A. A lot better, thanks.
B. That's a good idea.
C. Maybe you should use a heating pad.

**(*Track 44*) Listen to the conversation. Then listen to the question and three answers. What is the correct answer: A, B, or C?**

**5.** A. The man has a cold.
B. The man has the flu.
C. The man has a burn.

**6.** A. The woman was sick.
B. The woman's son was at school.
C. The woman's son had a cold.

# LIFE SKILLS I

***(Track 45)*** **Look at the pictures and listen. What is the correct answer: A, B, or C?**

**7.**

Appointment
CITY CLINIC

Date: March 1
Time: 2:00 P.M.
Mon. Tues. (Wed.) Thurs. Fri.

**A**

Appointment
CITY CLINIC

Date: March 2
Time: 1:00 P.M.
Mon. Tues. (Wed.) Thurs. Fri.

**B**

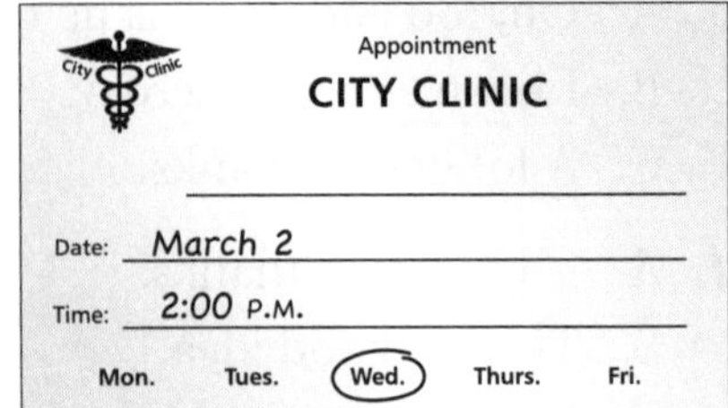

Appointment
CITY CLINIC

Date: March 2
Time: 2:00 P.M.
Mon. Tues. (Wed.) Thurs. Fri.

**C**

**8.**

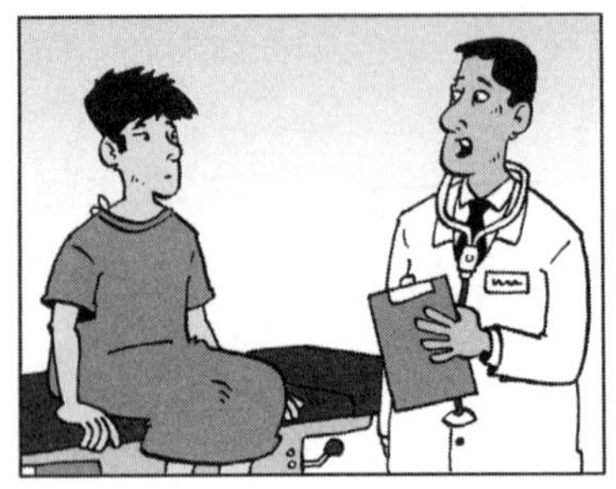

**A**

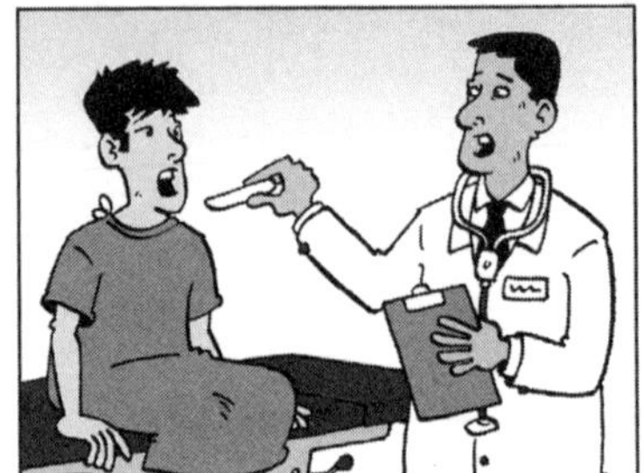

**B**

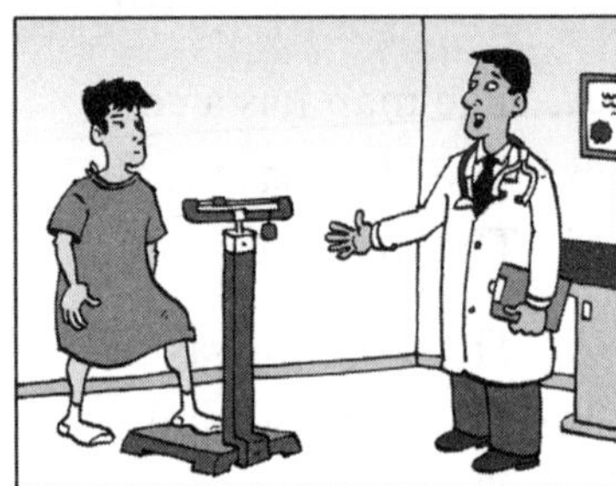

**C**

NAME ____________________

# GRAMMAR

## Complete each conversation. What is the correct answer: A, B, or C?

**9. A:** Do you ______ a fever?
**B:** No, I don't. I have a sore throat.

A. has
B. have
C. do

**10. A:** I have the flu.
**B:** Oh, no. You ______ go to school.

A. are
B. should
C. shouldn't

**11. A:** Does she ______ a toothache?
**B:** Yes, she does.

A. have
B. has
C. feels

**12. A:** Are Bancha and Jaidee in class today?
**B:** Yes, but they ______ here yesterday. They were absent.

A. was
B. wasn't
C. weren't

**13. A:** Michelle ______ at work yesterday.
**B:** I know. She was home sick.

A. was
B. wasn't
C. weren't

**14. A:** It's cold and windy.
**B:** Yes. Tim and Susan ______ wear jackets.

A. should
B. shouldn't
C. have

**15. A:** How does Long feel today?
**B:** He doesn't ______ well.

A. have
B. feels
C. feel

**16. A:** Where were you and your sister yesterday?
**B:** We ______ home sick.

A. are
B. was
C. were

**17. A:** How are your brothers?
**B:** They're fine today, but they ______ sick last week.

A. weren't
B. are
C. were

**18. A:** Mario feels terrible.
**B:** Really? He ______ go to work.

A. isn't
B. don't
C. shouldn't

**19. A:** Does she have a cough?
**B:** Yes, she ______.

A. do
B. does
C. doesn't

**20. A:** How does your daughter feel?
**B:** She ______ a lot better now.

A. feels
B. feel
C. doesn't

**21. A:** Kevin shouldn't play soccer today.
**B:** You're right. He ______ rest.

A. shouldn't
B. should
C. have

**22. A:** Carlos ______ sick last night.
**B:** Oh. Is he OK today?

A. was
B. is
C. were

**23. A:** Grandma, you ______ take your medicine now.
**B:** OK. Where is it?

A. are
B. shouldn't
C. should

NAME ____________________

# VOCABULARY

**Read. What is the correct answer: A, B, C, or D?**

**24.** Clap your hands.

A. ①

B. ②

C. ③

D. ④

**25.** Nod your head.

A. ①

B. ②

C. ③

D. ④

**26.** Touch your knee.

A. ①

B. ②

C. ③

D. ④

NAME ______________________

**Read. What is the correct answer: A, B, C, or D?**

**27.** How does Raymond feel?

A. His eye hurts.

B. His nose hurts.

C. His teeth hurt.

D. His elbow hurts.

NAME ____________________

# LIFE SKILLS II

## Read. What is the correct answer: A, B, C, or D?

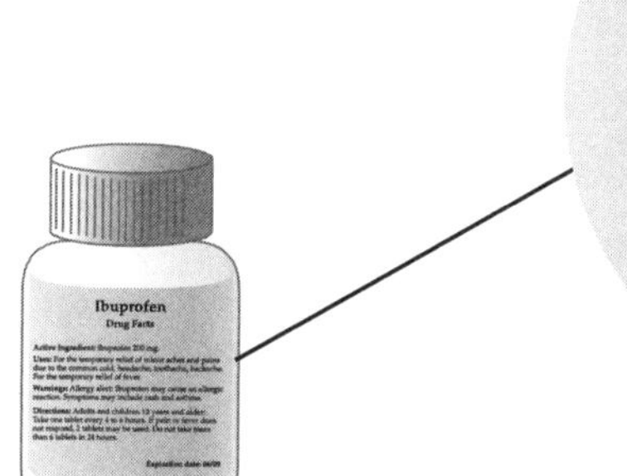

**IBUPROFEN**

Pain Reliever/Fever Reducer

**Directions:** Take one tablet every 3 to 5 hours.

**Warnings:**
- Take with food.
- Do not drink alcoholic beverages.
- Do not give to children under 6.

**28.** How often should you take this medicine?

A. twice a day

B. once a day

C. every 3 to 5 hours

D. every 5 to 7 hours

**29.** Who is this medicine for?

A. adults only

B. babies

C. children under 6

D. children over 6 and adults

NAME ____________________

**Read. What is the correct answer: A, B, C, or D?**

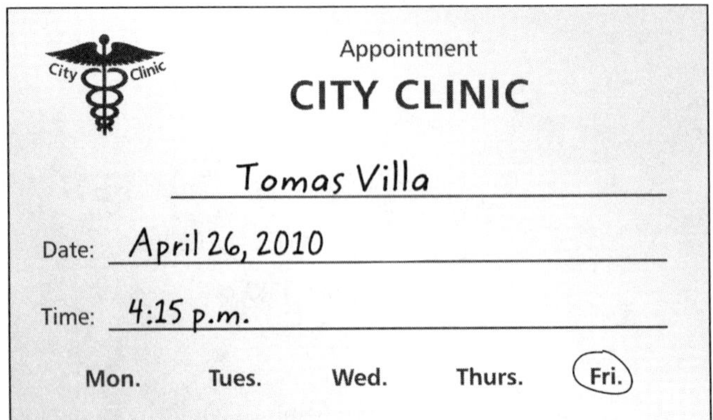
Appointment

CITY CLINIC

Tomas Villa

Date: April 26, 2010

Time: 4:15 p.m.

Mon. Tues. Wed. Thurs. Fri.

**30.** Who is the appointment for?

A. Tomas Villa

B. City Clinic

C. April 26

D. Friday

**31.** When is the appointment?

A. Friday, April 25, at 4:00 P.M.

B. Friday, April 26, at 4:15 P.M.

C. Monday, August 26, at 4:15 A.M.

D. Friday, August 26, at 4:15 P.M.

# READING

## Read. What is the correct answer: A, B, C, or D?

Bill wasn't at work yesterday. He was home in bed. Today his throat hurts, and he is at home. Bill still has a headache, but he doesn't have a fever. His son, Mason, is at home too. He doesn't feel well. He has a fever. Bill and Mason have an appointment at City Clinic at 10:30 tomorrow morning.

**32.** Where are Bill and Mason today?
- A. at work
- B. at home
- C. at school
- D. at the City Clinic

**33.** What is the problem with Mason?
- A. He feels well.
- B. His throat hurts.
- C. He has a headache.
- D. He has a fever.

NAME ____________________

# Unit 12 Test

## LISTENING I

***(Track 46)*** **Look at the pictures and listen. What is the correct answer: A, B, or C?**

1.

**A**

**B**

**C**

2.

**A**

**B**

**C**

# LISTENING II

**(Track 47) Listen to the question and three answers. What is the correct answer: A, B, or C?**

**3.** A. Two years.
B. I was a sales assistant.
C. This place looks great!

**4.** A. No, I can't, but I can learn.
B. OK, I can work Saturday.
C. Listen, I need a favor.

**(Track 48) Listen to the conversation. Then listen to the question and three answers. What is the correct answer: A, B, or C?**

**5.** A. Thursday from 1:00 to 6:00
B. Friday from 12:00 to 5:00
C. Friday from 1:00 to 6:00

**6.** A. four years
B. fourteen years
C. fifteen years

NAME ______________________________

## GRAMMAR

### Complete each conversation. What is the correct answer: A, B, or C?

**7. A:** Maria ______ English. How about you?
**B:** I can, too.

A. can
B. speak
C. can speak

**8. A:** ______ Kai at the bank?
**B:** Three years.

A. How long
B. How long is
C. How long was

**9. A:** Celine can't answer phones.
**B:** No, but she ______ make copies.

A. can't
B. isn't
C. can

**10. A:** ______ take care of grounds?
**B:** Yes, they can.

A. Can
B. Your brothers can
C. Can your brothers

**11. A:** ______ you use a computer?
**B:** Yes, I can. I use a computer at work every day.

A. Can
B. Were
C. How long

**12. A:** Can Nicolai and Andrei pick up packages at the post office?
**B:** No, they ______. They're busy today.

A. can't
B. can
C. were

**13. A:** ______ David a carpenter?
**B:** No, he wasn't. He was a sales assistant.

A. Is
B. Was
C. Were

14. **A:** Were you happy at the department store?
**B:** No, I ______.

A. wasn't
B. was
C. am

15. **A:** How long ______ you at Buena Vista Restaurant?
**B:** Six years. From 2001 to 2007.

A. was
B. can
C. were

16. **A:** Can your sons lift heavy boxes?
**B:** Yes, ______.

A. they can
B. they can't
C. can

17. **A:** Can Franco fix trucks?
**B:** No. But he ______ cars.

A. fix
B. can fix
C. can't

18. **A:** I can deliver packages. What about you?
**B:** I ______ packages, but I can lift heavy boxes.

A. can
B. can't
C. can't deliver

19. **A:** Can Amine use a cash register?
**B:** Yes, ______.

A. she can
B. she can't
C. she is

20. **A:** Was Enrique at work this afternoon?
**B:** No, he ______.

A. can't
B. wasn't
C. isn't

21. **A:** Paulo ______ cabinets.
**B:** Really?

A. can't
B. can make
C. can

# VOCABULARY

## Read. What is the correct answer: A, B, C, or D?

**22.** What does Ned do at work?

A. He cleans floors.

B. He answers the phone.

C. He takes care of grounds.

D. He lifts heavy boxes.

NAME ______________________

**Read. What is the correct answer: A, B, C, or D?**

**23.** What does Meiling do at work every day?

A. She uses a computer.

B. She drives a truck.

C. She picks up packages.

D. She fixes things.

## Read. What is the correct answer: A, B, C, or D?

①

②

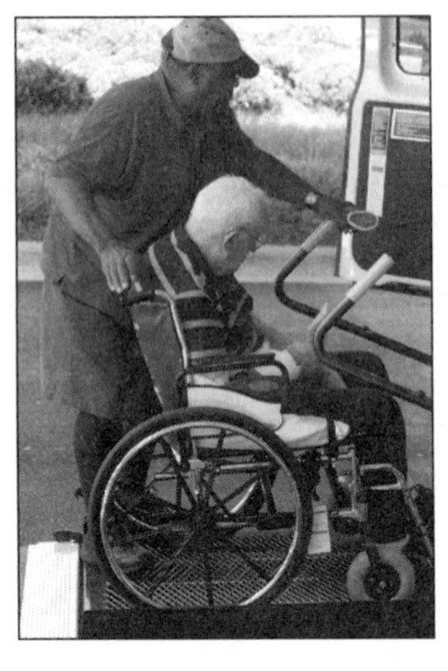

③

④

**24.** Alex helps people.

A. ①
B. ②
C. ③
D. ④

**25.** Lee delivers packages.

A. ①
B. ②
C. ③
D. ④

NAME ____________________

# LIFE SKILLS

## Read. What is the correct answer: A, B, C, or D?

| ① | ② | ③ | ④ |
|---|---|---|---|
| GRANDPA'S RESTAURANT<br>FT Waiters<br>Exp. nec.<br>M–F 6:00 A.M.–2:00 P.M.<br>Apply in person<br>13 Baker St. | PLUMBERS<br>PT. $18/hr<br>Exp. nec.<br>Call Gabe:<br>(562) 666-4321 | BARTELMANNS REAL ESTATE BROKERS<br>FT Office Assistant<br>Exp. nec.<br>FAX: Nan Redman<br>(562) 333-5678 | METRO INSURANCE CORP.<br>FT Security Guard, night shift<br>$15/hr<br>Apply in person.<br>1435 Pendleton St. |

**26.** What are the work hours for the waiter job?

A. Monday from 6:00 in the morning to 2:00 in the afternoon

B. Monday–Friday, from 6:00 in the evening to 2:00 in the morning

C. Monday to Friday, from 6:00 in the morning to 2:00 in the afternoon

D. Monday and Friday, from 6:00 in the evening to 2:00 in the morning

**27.** Which job does **not** need someone with experience?

A. ①

B. ②

C. ③

D. ④

**28.** Which job is for the night shift only?

A. ①

B. ②

C. ③

D. ④

**29.** Which job is part-time?

A. ①

B. ②

C. ③

D. ④

**30.** How can you apply for the office assistant job?

A. call

B. send a fax

C. go to the office

D. mail a letter

NAME ____________________

# READING

## Read. What is the correct answer: A, B, C, or D?

Nellie needs help with her bookstore. Nellie can use a cash register, but she can't fix things. She can't lift heavy boxes. Pedro can fix things and lift heavy boxes. So Pedro works in Nellie's store. Pedro was a cook for five years, but now he's a sales assistant. He loves it!

**31.** What can Nellie do?

A. She can use a computer.

B. She can use a cash register.

C. She can fix things.

D. She can lift heavy boxes.

**32.** What was Pedro's last job?

A. He was a sales assistant.

B. He was a waiter.

C. He was a cashier.

D. He was a cook.

**33.** Where do Pedro and Nellie work now?

A. in a department store

B. in a restaurant

C. in a bookstore

D. in a factory

# Future 1
# Unit Test Answer Sheet

① ______________________________
Last Name First Name Middle

② ______________________________
Teacher's Name

TEST

1 (A) (B) (C) (D)
2 (A) (B) (C) (D)
3 (A) (B) (C) (D)
4 (A) (B) (C) (D)
5 (A) (B) (C) (D)
6 (A) (B) (C) (D)
7 (A) (B) (C) (D)
8 (A) (B) (C) (D)
9 (A) (B) (C) (D)
10 (A) (B) (C) (D)
11 (A) (B) (C) (D)
12 (A) (B) (C) (D)
13 (A) (B) (C) (D)
14 (A) (B) (C) (D)
15 (A) (B) (C) (D)
16 (A) (B) (C) (D)
17 (A) (B) (C) (D)
18 (A) (B) (C) (D)
19 (A) (B) (C) (D)
20 (A) (B) (C) (D)
21 (A) (B) (C) (D)
22 (A) (B) (C) (D)
23 (A) (B) (C) (D)
24 (A) (B) (C) (D)
25 (A) (B) (C) (D)
26 (A) (B) (C) (D)
27 (A) (B) (C) (D)
28 (A) (B) (C) (D)
29 (A) (B) (C) (D)
30 (A) (B) (C) (D)
31 (A) (B) (C) (D)
32 (A) (B) (C) (D)
33 (A) (B) (C) (D)

**Directions for marking answers**

- Use a No. 2 pencil. Do NOT use ink.
- Make dark marks and bubble in your answers completely.
- If you change an answer, erase your first mark completely.

Right
(A) (B) (C) (D)

Wrong
(A) (B) (C) (D)
(A) (B) (C) (D)

③ **STUDENT IDENTIFICATION**

| | | | | | | | | |
|---|---|---|---|---|---|---|---|---|
| 0 | 0 | 0 | 0 | 0 | 0 | 0 | 0 | 0 |
| 1 | 1 | 1 | 1 | 1 | 1 | 1 | 1 | 1 |
| 2 | 2 | 2 | 2 | 2 | 2 | 2 | 2 | 2 |
| 3 | 3 | 3 | 3 | 3 | 3 | 3 | 3 | 3 |
| 4 | 4 | 4 | 4 | 4 | 4 | 4 | 4 | 4 |
| 5 | 5 | 5 | 5 | 5 | 5 | 5 | 5 | 5 |
| 6 | 6 | 6 | 6 | 6 | 6 | 6 | 6 | 6 |
| 7 | 7 | 7 | 7 | 7 | 7 | 7 | 7 | 7 |
| 8 | 8 | 8 | 8 | 8 | 8 | 8 | 8 | 8 |
| 9 | 9 | 9 | 9 | 9 | 9 | 9 | 9 | 9 |

**Is this your Social Security number?**
**Yes** ☐ **No** ☐

④ **TEST DATE**

| MM | | D | D | Y | Y | Y |
|---|---|---|---|---|---|---|
| Jan | ☐ | 0 | 0 | 20 | 0 | 9 |
| Feb | ☐ | 1 | 1 | 20 | 1 | 0 |
| Mar | ☐ | 2 | 2 | 20 | 1 | 1 |
| Apr | ☐ | 3 | 3 | 20 | 1 | 2 |
| May | ☐ | | 4 | 20 | 1 | 3 |
| Jun | ☐ | | 5 | 20 | 1 | 4 |
| Jul | ☐ | | 6 | 20 | 1 | 5 |
| Aug | ☐ | | 7 | 20 | 1 | 6 |
| Sep | ☐ | | 8 | 20 | 1 | 7 |
| Oct | ☐ | | 9 | 20 | 1 | 8 |
| Nov | ☐ | | | | | |
| Dec | ☐ | | | | | |

⑤ **CLASS NUMBER**

| | | | | | | | |
|---|---|---|---|---|---|---|---|
| 0 | 0 | 0 | 0 | 0 | 0 | 0 | 0 |
| 1 | 1 | 1 | 1 | 1 | 1 | 1 | 1 |
| 2 | 2 | 2 | 2 | 2 | 2 | 2 | 2 |
| 3 | 3 | 3 | 3 | 3 | 3 | 3 | 3 |
| 4 | 4 | 4 | 4 | 4 | 4 | 4 | 4 |
| 5 | 5 | 5 | 5 | 5 | 5 | 5 | 5 |
| 6 | 6 | 6 | 6 | 6 | 6 | 6 | 6 |
| 7 | 7 | 7 | 7 | 7 | 7 | 7 | 7 |
| 8 | 8 | 8 | 8 | 8 | 8 | 8 | 8 |
| 9 | 9 | 9 | 9 | 9 | 9 | 9 | 9 |

⑥ **RAW SCORE**

| | |
|---|---|
| 0 | 0 |
| 1 | 1 |
| 2 | 2 |
| 3 | 3 |
| 4 | 4 |
| 5 | 5 |
| 6 | 6 |
| 7 | 7 |
| 8 | 8 |
| 9 | 9 |

# Unit 1 Test Answer Key

| | ANSWERS | LESSON/PAGE | OBJECTIVE |
|---|---|---|---|
| 1 | **A** B C D | 2/p. 9 | Introduce people |
| 2 | A B **C** D | 4/p. 13 | Identify people and ask where they are from |
| 3 | A **B** C D | 2/p. 9 | Introduce people |
| 4 | A B **C** D | 4/p. 13 | Identify people and ask where they are from |
| 5 | A B **C** D | 7/p. 19 | Talk about school |
| 6 | A **B** C D | 4/p. 13 | Identify people and ask where they are from |
| 7 | A B **C** D | 3/p. 11 | Say and spell a name |
| 8 | **A** B C D | 3/p. 11 | Say and spell a name |
| 9 | **A** B C D | 5/p. 14 | Affirmative of *be* with *I*, *he*, and *she* |
| 10 | A **B** C D | 5/p. 15 | Negative of *be* with *I*, *he*, and *she* |
| 11 | **A** B C D | 5/p. 14 | Affirmative of *be* with *I*, *he*, and *she* |
| 12 | A **B** C D | 8/p. 21 | Negative of *be* with *we*, *you*, *they*, and *it* |
| 13 | **A** B C D | 5/p. 15 | Negative of *be* with *I*, *he*, and *she* |
| 14 | A B **C** D | 8/p. 20 | Affirmative of *be* with *we*, *you*, *they*, and *it* |
| 15 | **A** B C D | 8/p. 21 | Negative of *be* with *we*, *you*, *they*, and *it* |
| 16 | A B **C** D | 8/p. 20 | Affirmative of *be* with *we*, *you*, *they*, and *it* |
| 17 | A B **C** D | 8/p. 21 | Negative of *be* with *we*, *you*, *they*, and *it* |
| 18 | A B **C** D | 8/p. 21 | Negative of *be* with *we*, *you*, *they*, and *it* |
| 19 | A **B** C D | 5/p. 14 | Affirmative of *be* with *I*, *he*, and *she* |
| 20 | A B **C** D | 8/p. 20 | Affirmative of *be* with *we*, *you*, *they*, and *it* |
| 21 | A **B** C D | 5/p. 15 | Negative of *be* with *I*, *he*, and *she* |
| 22 | A **B** C D | 8/p. 20 | Affirmative of *be* with *we*, *you*, *they*, and *it* |
| 23 | **A** B C D | 5/p. 14 | Affirmative of *be* with *I*, *he*, and *she* |
| 24 | **A** B C D | 1/p. 6 | Identify countries |
| 25 | A B **C** D | 1/p. 6 | Identify countries |
| 26 | **A** B C D | 1/p. 6 | Identify countries |
| 27 | A B **C** D | 1/p. 6 | Identify countries |
| 28 | A **B** C D | 3/p. 11 | Interpret a form |
| 29 | **A** B C D | 3/p. 11 | Interpret a form |
| 30 | A **B** C D | 3/p. 11 | Interpret a form |
| 31 | **A** B C D | | Read for details |
| 32 | A B **C** D | | Read for details |
| 33 | A B **C** D | | Read for details |

**Please see reverse for test audio script.**

# Unit 1 Test Audio Script

LISTENING I
(Track 5) Page 1. Look at the pictures and listen. What is the correct answer: A, B, or C?

1. Hi, I'm Mariam. I'm from Somalia.
2. That's Mr. Cordova.

LISTENING II
(Track 6) Page 2. Listen to the question and three answers. What is the correct answer: A, B, or C?

3. Where are you from?
   A. She is from Mexico.
   B. I'm from Poland.
   C. Yes, I am.

4. Who's that?
   A. I'm Miguel. I'm from El Salvador.
   B. Oh, you're right.
   C. That's Anh. She's from Vietnam.

(Track 7) Page 2. Listen to the conversation. Then listen to the question and three answers. What is the correct answer: A, B, or C?

5. **M:** How is English class?
   **F:** It's hard.

   How is the class?
   A. It's easy.
   B. It's friendly.
   C. It's hard.

6. **M:** That's the teacher.
   **F:** No, that's Galina. She's from Russia.

   Where is Galina from?
   A. She's from Somalia.
   B. She's from Russia.
   C. She's from China.

LIFE SKILLS I
(Track 8) Page 3. Look at the pictures and listen. What is the correct answer: A, B, or C?

7. **F:** What's your name?
   **M:** Karol Boruta.

8. **M:** How do you spell that?
   **F:** V-E-R-A.

# Unit 2 Test Answer Key

| | ANSWERS | LESSON/PAGE | OBJECTIVE |
|---|---|---|---|
| 1 | B | 2/p. 29 | Introduce someone and talk about a job |
| 2 | A | 5/p. 35 | Ask about jobs |
| 3 | C | 5/p. 35 | Ask about jobs |
| 4 | B | 8/p. 41 | Talk about where a person works |
| 5 | B | 2/p. 29 | Introduce someone and talk about a job |
| 6 | B | 5/p. 35 | Ask about jobs |
| 7 | A | 4/p. 32 | Give phone numbers |
| 8 | C | 4/p. 32 | Give phone numbers |
| 9 | C | 3/p. 30 | *A/an* |
| 10 | A | 6/p. 36 | *Be: Yes/no* questions and short answers |
| 11 | B | 6/p. 36 | *Be: Yes/no* questions and short answers |
| 12 | C | 3/p. 31 | Singular and plural nouns |
| 13 | C | 9/p. 42 | Simple present affirmative: *work* and *live* |
| 14 | A | 9/p. 42 | Simple present affirmative: *work* and *live* |
| 15 | B | 3/p. 31 | Singular and plural nouns |
| 16 | C | 6/p. 36 | *Be: Yes/no* questions and short answers |
| 17 | C | 9/p. 42 | Simple present affirmative: *work* and *live* |
| 18 | A | 9/p. 42 | Simple present affirmative: *work* and *live* |
| 19 | A | 3/p. 31 | Singular and plural nouns |
| 20 | A | 3/p. 30 | *A/an* |
| 21 | C | 3/p. 31 | Singular and plural nouns |
| 22 | A | 6/p. 36 | *Be: Yes/no* questions and short answers |
| 23 | A | 6/p. 36 | *Be: Yes/no* questions and short answers |
| 24 | A | 1/p. 26 | Identify jobs |
| 25 | D | 1/p. 26 | Identify jobs |
| 26 | B | 1/p. 26 | Identify jobs |
| 27 | D | 1/p. 26 | Identify jobs |
| 28 | B | 4/p. 33 | Give phone numbers |
| 29 | D | 4/p. 33 | Give phone numbers |
| 30 | C | 4/p. 33 | Give phone numbers |
| 31 | A | 4/p. 33 | Give phone numbers |
| 32 | C | | Read for details |
| 33 | B | | Read for details |

**Please see reverse for test audio script.**

# Unit 2 Test Audio Script

LISTENING I
(Track 9) Page 11. Look at the pictures and listen. What is the correct answer: A, B, or C?

1. I'm a sales assistant.
2. Who's that? Is she an electrician?

LISTENING II
(Track 10) Page 12. Listen to the question and three answers. What is the correct answer: A, B, or C?

3. What do you do?
   A. Thomas is a student.
   B. Oh, that's interesting.
   C. I'm a nurse.

4. Where do you work?
   A. I'm a caregiver.
   B. I work at a factory.
   C. No, I'm not.

(Track 11) Page 12. Listen to the conversation. Then listen to the question and three answers. What is the correct answer: A, B, or C?

5. **M:** I'm a student at Barnes College.
   **F:** Really? I'm a student there, too. And I'm a homemaker.

   Who is a homemaker?
   A. the man
   B. the woman
   C. the man and the woman

6. **M1:** Is Darla a driver?
   **M2:** No, she's not. She's an office assistant.

   Is the woman a driver?
   A. No, she's not. She's a cashier.
   B. No, she's not. She's an office assistant.
   C. Yes, she is.

LIFE SKILLS I
(Track 12) Page 13. Look at the pictures and listen. What is the correct answer: A, B, or C?

7. **M:** What's your phone number?
   **F:** 414-2334.

8. **M:** What's the area code?
   **F:** It's 555.

# Unit 3 Test Answer Key

| | ANSWERS | LESSON/PAGE | OBJECTIVE |
|---|---|---|---|
| 1 | C | 2/p. 48 | Give and follow classroom instructions |
| 2 | A | 5/p. 54 | Talk about things in the classroom |
| 3 | C | 2/p. 48 | Give and follow classroom instructions |
| 4 | A | 5/p. 54 | Talk about things in the classroom |
| 5 | A | 8/p. 60 | Talk about people and places at school |
| 6 | C | 8/p. 60 | Talk about people and places at school |
| 7 | B | 7/p. 59 | Talk about places at school |
| 8 | B | 7/p. 59 | Talk about places at school |
| 9 | A | 3/p. 50 | Imperatives |
| 10 | B | 6/p. 57 | *This, that, these, those:* Questions and answers |
| 11 | A | 6/p. 56 | *This, that, these, those:* Statements |
| 12 | A | 9/p. 62 | Object pronouns |
| 13 | B | 6/p. 57 | *This, that, these, those:* Questions and answers |
| 14 | B | 6/p. 57 | *This, that, these, those:* Questions and answers |
| 15 | A | 3/p. 50 | Imperatives |
| 16 | C | 6/p. 56 | *This, that, these, those:* Statements |
| 17 | A | 6/p. 57 | *This, that, these, those:* Questions and answers |
| 18 | C | 3/p. 50 | Imperatives |
| 19 | B | 6/p. 56 | *This, that, these, those:* Statements |
| 20 | B | 3/p. 50 | Imperatives |
| 21 | C | 6/p. 56 | *This, that, these, those:* Statements |
| 22 | A | 9/p. 62 | Object pronouns |
| 23 | C | 9/p. 62 | Object pronouns |
| 24 | A | 1/p. 46 | Identify things in the classroom |
| 25 | D | 1/p. 46 | Identify things in the classroom |
| 26 | D | 1/p. 47 | Identify things in the classroom |
| 27 | B | 1/p. 47 | Identify things in the classroom |
| 28 | D | 7/p. 59 | Identify places at school |
| 29 | D | 7/p. 59 | Identify places at school |
| 30 | D | 3/p. 50 | Interpret a form |
| 31 | D | 3/p. 50 | Interpret a form |
| 32 | C | | Read for details |
| 33 | C | | Read for details |

**Please see reverse for test audio script.**

# Unit 3 Test Audio Script

LISTENING I
(Track 13) Page 21. Look at the pictures and listen. What is the correct answer: A, B, or C?

1. Take out your book, please.
2. It's a CD.

LISTENING II
(Track 14) Page 22. Listen to the question and three answers. What is the correct answer: A, B, or C?

3. Can I borrow an eraser?
   A. It's a pencil.
   B. Take out an eraser.
   C. Sure.

4. What are these called in English?
   A. They're markers.
   B. Sure.
   C. Don't look at the exercise.

(Track 15) Page 22. Listen to the conversation. Then listen to the question and three answers. What is the correct answer: A, B, or C?

5. **M:** Is the library open?
   **F:** Yes, it is.

   What is open?
   A. The library.
   B. The computer lab.
   C. The book.

6. **M:** Who is she?
   **F:** She's the principal.

   Who is the woman?
   A. She's the teacher.
   B. She's the office assistant.
   C. She's the principal.

LIFE SKILLS I
(Track 16) Page 23. Look at the pictures and listen. What is the correct answer: A, B, or C?

7. **M:** Which way is the office?
   **F:** It's down the hall, across from the library.

8. **M:** Where is Room 18?
   **F:** It's next to the computer lab.

# Unit 4 Test Answer Key

| | ANSWERS | LESSON/PAGE | OBJECTIVE |
|---|---|---|---|
| 1 | B | 2/p. 68 | Talk about family members |
| 2 | C | 2/p. 68 | Talk about family members |
| 3 | B | 5/p. 74 | Describe people |
| 4 | A | 5/p. 74 | Describe people |
| 5 | B | 5/p. 74 | Describe people |
| 6 | B | 8/p. 80 | Give a child's age and grade in school |
| 7 | A | 7/p. 78 | Talk about months and dates |
| 8 | B | 3/p. 70 | Possessive adjectives |
| 9 | C | 3/p. 71 | Possessive nouns |
| 10 | A | 3/p. 70 | Possessive adjectives |
| 11 | B | 9/p. 82 | Questions with *How old* |
| 12 | B | 6/p. 76 | Descriptions with *have* |
| 13 | C | 6/p. 76 | Descriptions with *have* |
| 14 | A | 9/p. 82 | Questions with *How old* |
| 15 | B | 3/p. 71 | Possessive nouns |
| 16 | B | 6/p. 77 | Descriptions with *be* and *have* |
| 17 | B | 3/p. 70 | Possessive adjectives |
| 18 | B | 6/p. 77 | Descriptions with *be* and *have* |
| 19 | C | 6/p. 76 | Descriptions with *have* |
| 20 | C | 3/p. 71 | Possessive nouns |
| 21 | B | 9/p. 82 | Questions with *How old* |
| 22 | C | 6/p. 77 | Descriptions with *be* and *have* |
| 23 | C | 1/p. 66 | Identify family members |
| 24 | A | 1/p. 66 | Identify family members |
| 25 | C | 1/p. 66 | Identify family members |
| 26 | B | 1/p. 66 | Identify family members |
| 27 | B | 7/p. 78 | Interpret months and dates |
| 28 | B | 7/p. 79 | Interpret months and dates |
| 29 | C | 7/p. 79 | Interpret months and dates |
| 30 | A | | Read for details |
| 31 | B | | Read for details |
| 32 | C | | Read for details |
| 33 | C | | Read for details |

**Please see reverse for test audio script.**

# Unit 4 Test Audio Script

LISTENING I
(Track 17) Page 31. Look at the pictures and listen. What is the correct answer: A, B, or C?

1. Your mother looks nice.
2. This is Paula's father.

LISTENING II
(Track 18) Page 32. Listen to the question and three answers. What is the correct answer: A, B, or C?

3. Does your grandfather look like you?
   A. He's really friendly.
   B. No. He has a beard.
   C. He's seventy-five.

4. Is your family here in this country?
   A. My sister is here. She's a nurse.
   B. She looks like me.
   C. He's a gardener.

(Track 19) Page 32. Listen to the conversation. Then listen to the question and three answers. What is the correct answer: A, B, or C?

5. **M:** Pat, what's your sister like?
   **F:** She's nice.

   Who is nice?
   A. Pat's uncle
   B. Pat's sister
   C. Pat's brother

6. **F:** How old is the girl?
   **M:** She's twelve. She's in the sixth grade.

   What grade is the girl in?
   A. fifth grade
   B. sixth grade
   C. twelfth grade

LIFE SKILLS I
(Track 20) Page 33. Look at the pictures and listen. What is the correct answer: A, B, or C?

7. **F:** Chen, when is your birthday?
   **M:** My birthday is March seventeenth.

# Unit 5 Test Answer Key

| | ANSWERS | LESSON/PAGE | OBJECTIVE |
|---|---|---|---|
| 1 | A **B** C D | 5/p. 94 | Ask for sizes and colors |
| 2 | **A** B C D | 2/p. 88 | Talk about things someone needs or wants |
| 3 | **A** B C D | 5/p. 94 | Ask about sizes and colors |
| 4 | A **B** C D | 8/p. 100 | Return something to a store |
| 5 | A B **C** D | 8/p. 100 | Return something to a store |
| 6 | **A** B C D | 5/p. 94 | Ask for sizes and colors |
| 7 | **A** B C D | 4/p. 93 | Use U.S. money |
| 8 | A B **C** D | 4/p. 93 | Use U.S. money |
| 9 | **A** B C D | 3/p. 90 | Simple present affirmative |
| 10 | A **B** C D | 6/p. 96 | Simple present: *Yes/no* questions and short answers |
| 11 | A B **C** D | 9/p. 102 | Simple present negative |
| 12 | **A** B C D | 3/p. 90 | Simple present affirmative |
| 13 | A B **C** D | 3/p. 90 | Simple present affirmative |
| 14 | **A** B C D | 9/p. 102 | Simple present negative |
| 15 | A **B** C D | 6/p. 96 | Simple present: *Yes/no* questions and short answers |
| 16 | A B **C** D | 9/p. 102 | Simple present negative |
| 17 | A **B** C D | 9/p. 102 | Simple present negative |
| 18 | **A** B C D | 3/p. 90 | Simple present affirmative |
| 19 | **A** B C D | 6/p. 96 | Simple present: *Yes/no* questions and short answers |
| 20 | A B **C** D | 6/p. 96 | Simple present: *Yes/no* questions and short answers |
| 21 | A **B** C D | 9/p. 102 | Simple present negative |
| 22 | **A** B C D | 6/p. 96 | Simple present: *Yes/no* questions and short answers |
| 23 | A **B** C D | 3/p. 90 | Simple present affirmative |
| 24 | A B C **D** | 1/p. 86 | Identify colors and clothes |
| 25 | **A** B C D | 1/p. 86 | Identify colors and clothes |
| 26 | A **B** C D | 1/p. 86 | Identify colors and clothes |
| 27 | A B C **D** | 1/p. 86 | Identify clothes |
| 28 | A B **C** D | 4/p. 92 | Use U.S. money |
| 29 | A B C **D** | 4/p. 92 | Use U.S. money |
| 30 | A **B** C D | 4/p. 93 | Use U.S. money |
| 31 | A B C **D** | 4/p. 93 | Use U.S. money |
| 32 | A B **C** D | | Read for details |
| 33 | A **B** C D | | Read for details |

**Please see reverse for test audio script.**

# Unit 5 Test Audio Script

LISTENING I

(Track 21) Page 41. Look at the pictures and listen. What is the correct answer: A, B, or C?

1. Do you have this skirt in a large?
2. Leo wants a watch for his birthday.

LISTENING II

(Track 22) Page 42. Listen to the question and three answers. What is the correct answer: A, B, or C?

3. Does Roger like black sneakers?
   A. Yes, he does.
   B. He needs red socks.
   C. Too bad.

4. Hello. May I help you?
   A. No, I'm sorry. We don't.
   B. Hi. Yes. I need to return these shoes.
   C. Well, here you go.

(Track 23) Page 42. Listen to the conversation. Then listen to the question and three answers. What is the correct answer: A, B, or C?

5. **M:** What's the problem?
   **F:** This dress doesn't fit.

   What is the woman's problem?
   A. She doesn't have a receipt.
   B. The zipper on the dress doesn't work.
   C. The dress doesn't fit.

6. **F:** Do you have this shirt in a medium?
   **M:** Yes, we do. Here you go.

   What does the woman want?
   A. a medium shirt
   B. a small shirt
   C. a green T-shirt

LIFE SKILLS I

(Track 24) Page 43. Look at the pictures and listen. What is the correct answer: A, B, or C?

7. **F:** Excuse me. How much is this backpack?
   **M:** It's $20.

8. **M:** Excuse me. How much are these shoes?
   **F:** They're $40.99.

# Unit 6 Test Answer Key

| ANSWERS | LESSON/PAGE | OBJECTIVE |
|---|---|---|
| 1 B | 2/p. 108 | Talk about a house for rent |
| 2 C | 8/p. 120 | Give directions |
| 3 C | 5/p. 114 | Ask about an apartment for rent |
| 4 C | 5/p. 114 | Ask about an apartment for rent |
| 5 A | 2/p. 108 | Talk about a house for rent |
| 6 B | 5/p. 114 | Ask about an apartment for rent |
| 7 C | 7/p. 118 | Read addresses and apartment ads |
| 8 A | 3/p. 110 | *There is/There are* |
| 9 B | 3/p. 110 | *There is/There are* |
| 10 C | 3/p. 110 | *There is/There are* |
| 11 A | 6/p. 116 | *Is there/Are there* |
| 12 B | 6/p. 116 | *Is there/Are there* |
| 13 A | 6/p. 116 | *Is there/Are there* |
| 14 C | 9/p. 122 | Prepositions |
| 15 B | 9/p. 122 | Prepositions |
| 16 B | 9/p. 122 | Prepositions |
| 17 B | 6/p. 116 | *Is there/Are there* |
| 18 C | 9/p. 122 | Prepositions |
| 19 C | 9/p. 122 | Prepositions |
| 20 B | 3/p. 110 | *There is/There are* |
| 21 A | 3/p. 110 | *There is/There are* |
| 22 A | 6/p. 116 | *Is there/Are there* |
| 23 B | 1/p. 106 | Identify rooms and things in a house |
| 24 A | 1/p. 106 | Identify rooms and things in a house |
| 25 D | 1/p. 106 | Identify rooms and things in a house |
| 26 C | 1/p. 106 | Identify rooms and things in a house |
| 27 A | 7/p. 119 | Read addresses and apartment ads |
| 28 B | 7/p. 119 | Read addresses and apartment ads |
| 29 C | 7/p. 119 | Read addresses and apartment ads |
| 30 C | 7/p. 118 | Address an envelope |
| 31 D | 7/p. 118 | Address an envelope |
| 32 B | | Read for details |
| 33 C | | Read for details |

**Please see reverse for test audio script.**

# Unit 6 Test Audio Script

LISTENING I
(Track 25) Page 51. Look at the pictures and listen. What is the correct answer: A, B, or C?

1. There's a laundry room.
2. Continue on Fourth Street for 1 mile.

LISTENING II
(Track 26) Page 52. Listen to the question and three answers. What is the correct answer: A, B, or C?

3. Is there a one-bedroom apartment for rent in this building?
   A. Oh, great. Is it furnished?
   B. What about a dining room?
   C. Yes, it's on the third floor.

4. Are there appliances?
   A. Turn left on Sixth Avenue.
   B. Excuse me.
   C. Yes. There's a refrigerator.

(Track 27) Page 52. Listen to the conversation. Then listen to the question and three answers. What is the correct answer: A, B, or C?

5. **M:** What about a bathroom?
   **F:** Yes. There's a bathroom. It's sunny!

   What is the bathroom like?
   A. It's sunny.
   B. It's new.
   C. There is no bathroom.

6. **M:** Is the living room furnished?
   **F:** Yes. There's a sofa and a coffee table.

   What's in the living room?
   A. There's a coffee table, but no sofa.
   B. There's a sofa and a coffee table.
   C. There's a sofa, but no coffee table.

LIFE SKILLS I
(Track 28) Page 53. Look at the pictures and listen. What is the correct answer: A, B, or C?

7. **M:** What's your address?
   **F:** It's 222 North Main Street, Apartment 3.

# Unit 7 Test Answer Key

| ANSWERS | LESSON/PAGE | OBJECTIVE |
|---|---|---|
| 1 B | 8/p. 140 | Talk about feelings |
| 2 C | 5/p. 134 | Talk about weekend activities |
| 3 C | 5/p. 134 | Talk about weekend activities |
| 4 C | 2/p. 128 | Make plans with someone |
| 5 B | 2/p. 128 | Make plans with someone |
| 6 C | 8/p. 140 | Talk about how often a person does something |
| 7 B | 3/p. 130 | Simple present: Questions with *When* and *What time* |
| 8 B | 3/p. 130 | Simple present: Prepositions of time |
| 9 B | 6/p. 136 | Adverbs of frequency |
| 10 A | 3/p. 130 | Simple present: Prepositions of time |
| 11 C | 3/p. 130 | Simple present: Prepositions of time |
| 12 B | 3/p. 130 | Simple present: Prepositions of time |
| 13 C | 9/p. 142 | Simple present: Questions with *How often* |
| 14 C | 6/p. 136 | Adverbs of frequency |
| 15 B | 9/p. 142 | Simple present: Questions with *How often* |
| 16 A | 9/p. 142 | Simple present: Expressions of frequency |
| 17 B | 3/p. 130 | Simple present: Prepositions of time |
| 18 C | 9/p. 142 | Simple present: Questions with *How often* |
| 19 C | 3/p. 130 | Simple present: Questions with *When* and *What time* |
| 20 A | 6/p. 136 | Adverbs of frequency |
| 21 A | 6/p. 136 | Adverbs of frequency |
| 22 D | 1/p. 126 | Identify daily activities |
| 23 D | 1/p. 126 | Identify daily activities |
| 24 A | 1/p. 126 | Identify daily activities |
| 25 D | 1/p. 126 | Identify daily activities |
| 26 D | 4/p. 132 | Interpret work schedules and time sheets |
| 27 A | 4/p. 132 | Interpret work schedules and time sheets |
| 28 C | 4/p. 132 | Interpret work schedules and time sheets |
| 29 C | 4/p. 133 | Interpret work schedules and time sheets |
| 30 D | 4/p. 133 | Interpret work schedules and time sheets |
| 31 D | 4/p. 133 | Interpret work schedules and time sheets |
| 32 B | | Read for details |
| 33 D | | Read for details |

**Please see reverse for test audio script.**

# Unit 7 Test Audio Script

LISTENING I
(Track 29) Page 60. Look at the pictures and listen. What is the correct answer: A, B, or C?

1. They look bored.
2. I usually play basketball on Fridays.

LISTENING II
(Track 30) Page 61. Listen to the question and three answers. What is the correct answer: A, B, or C?

3. What do you usually do on the weekend?
   A. Me, too.
   B. At 8:00.
   C. I always do the laundry.

4. When do you get home?
   A. Are you free tomorrow?
   B. That's a good idea.
   C. At 5:00.

(Track 31) Page 61. Listen to the conversation. Then listen to the question and three answers. What is the correct answer: A, B, or C?

5. **F:** Jeff, are you free tomorrow? How about a movie?
   **M:** Sorry, I'm busy. I visit my family on Sundays.

   Is Jeff free tomorrow?
   A. Yes, he is.
   B. No, he isn't. He visits his family on Sundays.
   C. No, he isn't. He goes to movies on Sundays.

6. **F:** I exercise every day to relax.
   **M:** That's a good idea. I never exercise.

   How often does the man exercise?
   A. every day
   B. every weekend
   C. never

# Unit 8 Test Answer Key

| | ANSWERS | LESSON/PAGE | OBJECTIVE |
|---|---|---|---|
| 1 | B | 5/p. 154 | Order a meal in a restaurant |
| 2 | C | 2/p. 149 | Talk about food likes and dislikes |
| 3 | A | 5/p. 154 | Order a meal in a restaurant |
| 4 | C | 8/p. 160 | Plan a healthy meal |
| 5 | B | 8/p. 160 | Plan a healthy meal |
| 6 | B | 5/p. 154 | Order a meal in a restaurant |
| 7 | B | 7/p. 157 | Compare food prices |
| 8 | B | 7/p. 157 | Compare food prices |
| 9 | B | 3/p. 150 | Count and non-count nouns |
| 10 | A | 3/p. 150 | Count and non-count nouns |
| 11 | B | 9/p. 162 | Simple present: Questions with *How many* and *How much* |
| 12 | C | 3/p. 150 | Count and non-count nouns |
| 13 | C | 6/p. 156 | Choice questions with *or* |
| 14 | B | 6/p. 156 | Choice questions with *or* |
| 15 | A | 9/p. 162 | Simple present: Questions with *How many* and *How much* |
| 16 | A | 6/p. 156 | Choice questions with *or* |
| 17 | C | 9/p. 162 | Simple present: Questions with *How many* and *How much* |
| 18 | A | 9/p. 162 | Simple present: Questions with *How many* and *How much* |
| 19 | A | 3/p. 150 | Count and non-count nouns |
| 20 | B | 3/p. 150 | Count and non-count nouns |
| 21 | C | 6/p. 156 | Choice questions with *or* |
| 22 | B | 9/p. 162 | Simple present: Questions with *How many* and *How much* |
| 23 | A | 3/p. 150 | Count and non-count nouns |
| 24 | C | 1/p. 146 | Identify common foods |
| 25 | B | 1/p. 146 | Identify common foods |
| 26 | D | 1/p. 146 | Identify common foods |
| 27 | C | 1/p. 146 | Identify common foods |
| 28 | C | 7/p. 159 | Read food labels |
| 29 | D | 7/p. 159 | Read food labels |
| 30 | A | 7/p. 158 | Understand nutrition |
| 31 | D | 7/p. 158 | Understand nutrition |
| 32 | B | | Read for details |
| 33 | D | | Read for details |

**Please see reverse for test audio script.**

# Unit 8 Test Audio Script

LISTENING I
(Track 32) Page 70. Look at the pictures and listen. What is the correct answer: A, B, or C?

**1.** I'd like a turkey sandwich.
**2.** I don't really like tacos, but I love steak!

LISTENING II
(Track 33) Page 71. Listen to the question and three answers. What is the correct answer: A, B, or C?

**3.** Can I help you?
A. Yes, I'd like a green salad and a cup of coffee.
B. Large, please.
C. Coffee is good.

**4.** Let's have salmon for dinner.
A. Two pounds.
B. What about you?
C. OK. How much salmon do we need?

(Track 34) Page 71. Listen to the conversation. Then listen to the question and three answers. What is the correct answer: A, B, or C?

**5.** **F:** Let's have cucumber in the salad.
**M:** Oh, I don't like cucumbers.

What's the problem?
A. The man likes soup.
B. The man doesn't like cucumbers.
C. The man doesn't like salad.

**6.** **F:** Anything else?
**M:** Yes, an iced tea, please.

What does the man want?
A. pizza
B. iced tea
C. cheese

LIFE SKILLS I
(Track 35). Page 72. Look at the pictures and listen. What is the correct answer: A, B, or C?

**7.** **F:** Where are bananas cheaper, at Farmer John's or at Mary's Market?
**M:** Farmer John's. They're 89¢ a pound.

**8.** **F:** Where is milk cheaper, Best Food Buy or Mary's Market?
**M:** Best Food Buy. It's $1.69.

# Unit 9 Test Answer Key

| | ANSWERS | LESSON/PAGE | OBJECTIVE |
|---|---|---|---|
| 1 | A **B** C D | 2/p. 168 | Talk about what is happening now |
| 2 | **A** B C D | 8/p. 180 | Understand a weather report |
| 3 | A B **C** D | 2/p. 168 | Talk about what is happening now |
| 4 | A B **C** D | 8/p. 180 | Understand a weather report |
| 5 | A **B** C D | 5/p. 174 | Ask what someone is doing now |
| 6 | A B **C** D | 5/p. 174 | Talk about what is happening now |
| 7 | A B **C** D | 3/p. 170 | Present continuous: Statements |
| 8 | **A** B C D | 6/p. 176 | Present continuous: *Yes/no* questions and short answers |
| 9 | A B **C** D | 9/p. 182 | Adverbs of degree: *Very, really, pretty* |
| 10 | A B **C** D | 6/p. 176 | Present continuous: *Yes/no* questions and short answers |
| 11 | A **B** C D | 6/p. 170 | Present continuous: Statements |
| 12 | A **B** C D | 9/p. 182 | Adverbs of degree: *Very, really, pretty* |
| 13 | **A** B C D | 9/p. 182 | Adverbs of degree: *Very, really, pretty* |
| 14 | A **B** C D | 3/p. 170 | Present continuous: Statements |
| 15 | A **B** C D | 9/p. 182 | Adverbs of degree: *Very, really, pretty* |
| 16 | A B **C** D | 3/p. 170 | Present continuous: Statements |
| 17 | A B **C** D | 6/p. 176 | Present continuous: *Yes/no* questions and short answers |
| 18 | A **B** C D | 6/p. 176 | Present continuous: *Yes/no* questions and short answers |
| 19 | A B **C** D | 9/p. 182 | Adverbs of degree: *Very, really, pretty* |
| 20 | A **B** C D | 6/p. 176 | Present continuous: *Yes/no* questions and short answers |
| 21 | **A** B C D | 6/p. 176 | Present continuous: *Yes/no* questions and short answers |
| 22 | A **B** C D | 1/p. 166 | Identify weather and seasons |
| 23 | A B C **D** | 1/p. 166 | Identify weather and seasons |
| 24 | A B C **D** | 1/p. 166 | Identify weather and seasons |
| 25 | A **B** C D | 1/p. 166 | Identify weather and seasons |
| 26 | A **B** C D | 4/p. 172 | Plan for an emergency |
| 27 | **A** B C D | 4/p. 172 | Plan for an emergency |
| 28 | A **B** C D | 4/p. 173 | Plan for an emergency |
| 29 | A B C **D** | 4/p. 173 | Plan for an emergency |
| 30 | A **B** C D | 4/p. 173 | Plan for an emergency |
| 31 | A B **C** D | 4/p. 173 | Plan for an emergency |
| 32 | A **B** C D | | Read for details |
| 33 | A B **C** D | | Read for details |

**Please see reverse for test audio script.**

# Unit 9 Test Audio Script

LISTENING I
(Track 36) Page 80. Look at the pictures and listen. What is the correct answer: A, B, or C?

1. It's rainy.
2. It's hot today!

LISTENING II
(Track 37) Page 81. Listen to the question and three answers. What is the correct answer: A, B, or C?

3. How's the weather in Denver?
   A. Yes. Why?
   B. I'm in Denver.
   C. It's cold and rainy.

4. It's very sunny.
   A. I'm shopping.
   B. No, I'm not.
   C. That's OK. I have sunblock.

(Track 38) Page 81. Listen to the conversation. Then listen to the question and three answers. What is the correct answer: A, B, or C?

5. **M:** Are you checking e-mail?
   **F:** No, I'm not. I'm watching the weather on TV.

   What is the woman doing?
   A. She's reading.
   B. She's watching TV.
   C. She's checking e-mail.

6. **M:** A snowstorm is coming.
   **F:** Really?

   What is coming?
   A. a hurricane
   B. a thunderstorm
   C. a snowstorm

# Unit 10 Test Answer Key

| | ANSWERS | LESSON/PAGE | OBJECTIVE |
|---|---|---|---|
| 1 | B | 2/p. 188 | Give locations of places in the community |
| 2 | B | 5/p. 194 | Ask about bus routes and costs |
| 3 | C | 5/p. 194 | Ask about bus routes and costs |
| 4 | A | 8/p. 200 | Talk about weekend plans |
| 5 | C | 8/p. 200 | Talk about weekend plans |
| 6 | B | 5/p. 194 | Ask about bus routes and costs |
| 7 | C | 3/p. 190 | Prepositions of place |
| 8 | C | 6/p. 196 | Simple present: Questions with *How*, *How much*, and *Where* |
| 9 | B | 3/p. 190 | Prepositions of place |
| 10 | A | 6/p. 196 | Simple present: Questions with *How*, *How much*, and *Where* |
| 11 | C | 3/p. 190 | Prepositions of place |
| 12 | A | 6/p. 196 | Simple present: Questions with *How*, *How much*, and *Where* |
| 13 | B | 9/p. 202 | Present continuous for future |
| 14 | A | 3/p. 190 | Prepositions of place |
| 15 | B | 9/p. 202 | Present continuous for future |
| 16 | A | 6/p. 196 | Simple present: Questions with *How*, *How much*, and *Where* |
| 17 | B | 6/p. 196 | Simple present: Questions with *How*, *How much*, and *Where* |
| 18 | C | 9/p. 202 | Present continuous for future |
| 19 | A | 9/p. 202 | Present continuous for future |
| 20 | C | 3/p. 190 | Prepositions of place |
| 21 | B | 9/p. 202 | Present continuous for future |
| 22 | A | 1/p. 186 | Identify places in the community |
| 23 | C | 1/p. 186 | Identify places in the community |
| 24 | B | 2/p. 189 | Identify places in the community |
| 25 | D | 1/p. 186 | Identify places in the community |
| 26 | B | 4/p. 191 | Identify types of transportation |
| 27 | A | 4/p. 191 | Identify types of transportation |
| 28 | C | 4/p. 192 | Interpret signs |
| 29 | B | 4/p. 193 | Interpret schedules |
| 30 | D | 4/p. 193 | Interpret schedules |
| 31 | D | 4/p. 193 | Interpret schedules |
| 32 | A | | Read for details |
| 33 | D | | Read for details |

**Please see reverse for test audio script.**

# Unit 10 Test Audio Script

LISTENING I
(Track 39) Page 90. Look at the pictures and listen. What is the correct answer: A, B, or C?

1. Excuse me. I'm looking for a coffee shop.
2. You need exact change.

LISTENING II
(Track 40) Page 91. Listen to the question and three answers. What is the correct answer: A, B, or C?

3. How much does the bus cost?
   A. Can you help me?
   B. Sure.
   C. One dollar.

4. Where's the grand opening?
   A. At Greenville Shopping Mall.
   B. I'm going to a yard sale.
   C. Sounds great.

(Track 41) Page 91. Listen to the conversation. Then listen to the question and three answers. What is the correct answer: A, B, or C?

5. **F:** What are you doing this weekend?
   **M:** I'm going to a baseball game.

   What is the man doing this weekend?
   A. He's going to a concert.
   B. He's going to a yard sale.
   C. He's going to a baseball game.

6. **F:** Excuse me. How do you get to the courthouse?
   **M:** Take the number 2 bus, and get off at Third Street.

   Where does the woman want to go?
   A. to the community college
   B. to the courthouse
   C. to a coffee shop

# Unit 11 Test Answer Key

| | ANSWERS | LESSON/PAGE | OBJECTIVE |
|---|---|---|---|
| 1 | A | 2/p. 208 | Call to explain an absence |
| 2 | A | 2/p. 208 | Call to explain an absence |
| 3 | A | 5/p. 214 | Talk about the past |
| 4 | C | 8/p. 220 | Give advice |
| 5 | B | 8/p. 220 | Give advice |
| 6 | C | 5/p. 214 | Talk about the past |
| 7 | B | 4/p. 211 | Read an appointment card |
| 8 | A | 4/p. 212 | Understand instructions for a medical exam |
| 9 | B | 3/p. 210 | Review: Simple present |
| 10 | C | 9/p. 222 | *Should:* Statements |
| 11 | A | 3/p. 210 | Review: Simple present |
| 12 | C | 6/p. 216 | Past of *be*: Statements |
| 13 | B | 6/p. 216 | Past of *be*: Statements |
| 14 | A | 9/p. 222 | *Should:* Statements |
| 15 | C | 3/p. 210 | Review: Simple present |
| 16 | C | 6/p. 216 | Past of *be*: Statements |
| 17 | C | 6/p. 216 | Past of *be*: Statements |
| 18 | C | 9/p. 222 | *Should:* Statements |
| 19 | B | 3/p. 210 | Review: Simple present |
| 20 | A | 3/p. 210 | Review: Simple present |
| 21 | B | 9/p. 222 | *Should:* Statements |
| 22 | A | 6/p. 216 | Past of *be*: Statements |
| 23 | C | 9/p. 222 | *Should:* Statements |
| 24 | C | 1/p. 206 | Identify parts of the body |
| 25 | A | 1/p. 206 | Identify parts of the body |
| 26 | D | 1/p. 206 | Identify parts of the body |
| 27 | C | 1/p. 206 | Identify parts of the body |
| 28 | C | 4/p. 213 | Interpret medicine labels |
| 29 | D | 4/p. 213 | Interpret medicine labels |
| 30 | A | 4/p. 211 | Read an appointment card |
| 31 | B | 4/p. 211 | Read an appointment card |
| 32 | B | | Read for details |
| 33 | D | | Read for details |

**Please see reverse for test audio script.**

# Unit 11 Test Audio Script

LISTENING I
(Track 42) Page 100. Look at the pictures and listen. What is the correct answer: A, B, or C?

1. He has a stuffy nose.
2. I have an earache.

LISTENING II
(Track 43) Page 101. Listen to the question and three answers. What is the correct answer: A, B, or C?

3. My husband was home sick yesterday.
   A. Oh, too bad. How is he today?
   B. I wasn't here yesterday.
   C. A lot better, thanks.

4. I have a terrible backache.
   A. A lot better, thanks.
   B. That's a good idea.
   C. Maybe you should use a heating pad.

(Track 44) Page 101. Listen to the conversation. Then listen to the question and three answers. What is the correct answer: A, B, or C?

5. **M:** I have the flu.
   **F:** You should stay in bed and drink a lot.

   What's the problem?
   A. The man has a cold.
   B. The man has the flu.
   C. The man has a burn.

6. **M:** You weren't here yesterday.
   **F:** I know. My son was home sick. He had a cold.

   What happened yesterday?
   A. The woman was sick.
   B. The woman's son was at school.
   C. The woman's son had a cold.

LIFE SKILLS I
(Track 45) Page 102. Look at the pictures and listen. What is the correct answer: A, B, or C?

7. **M:** I'd like to make an appointment for a checkup.
   **F:** OK. How about Wednesday, March 2nd, at 1:00 P.M.?

8. **M1:** Look straight ahead.
   **M2:** OK, Dr. Cifuentes.

# Unit 12 Test Answer Key

| | ANSWERS | LESSON/PAGE | OBJECTIVE |
|---|---|---|---|
| 1 | B | 2/p. 228 | Respond to a Help Wanted sign |
| 2 | B | 8/p. 240 | Talk about work experience |
| 3 | B | 8/p. 240 | Talk about work experience |
| 4 | A | 2/p. 228 | Respond to a Help Wanted sign |
| 5 | C | 5/p. 234 | Talk about hours a person can work |
| 6 | B | 8/p. 240 | Talk about work experience |
| 7 | C | 3/p. 230 | *Can*: Statements |
| 8 | C | 9/p. 242 | Past of *be*: Questions and answers |
| 9 | C | 3/p. 230 | *Can*: Statements |
| 10 | C | 6/p. 236 | *Can*: *Yes/no* questions and short answers |
| 11 | A | 6/p. 236 | *Can*: *Yes/no* questions and short answers |
| 12 | A | 6/p. 236 | *Can*: *Yes/no* questions and short answers |
| 13 | B | 9/p. 242 | Past of *be*: Questions and answers |
| 14 | A | 9/p. 242 | Past of *be*: Questions and answers |
| 15 | C | 9/p. 242 | Past of *be*: Questions and answers |
| 16 | A | 6/p. 236 | *Can*: *Yes/no* questions and short answers |
| 17 | B | 3/p. 230 | *Can*: Statements |
| 18 | C | 3/p. 230 | *Can*: Statements |
| 19 | A | 6/p. 236 | *Can*: *Yes/no* questions and short answers |
| 20 | B | 9/p. 242 | Past of *be*: Questions and answers |
| 21 | B | 3/p. 230 | *Can*: Statements |
| 22 | C | 1/p. 226 | Identify job duties |
| 23 | A | 1/p. 226 | Identify job duties |
| 24 | C | 1/p. 226 | Identify job duties |
| 25 | D | 1/p. 226 | Identify job duties |
| 26 | C | 4/p. 232 | Read want ads |
| 27 | D | 4/p. 232 | Read want ads |
| 28 | D | 4/p. 232 | Read want ads |
| 29 | B | 4/p. 232 | Read want ads |
| 30 | B | 4/p. 232 | Read want ads |
| 31 | B | | Read for details |
| 32 | D | | Read for details |
| 33 | C | | Read for details |

**Please see reverse for test audio script.**

# Unit 12 Test Audio Script

LISTENING I
(Track 46) Page 110. Look at the pictures and listen. What is the correct answer: A, B, or C?

**1.** I can fix things.
**2.** I was a cashier.

LISTENING II
(Track 47) Page 111. Listen to the question and three answers. What is the correct answer: A, B, or C?

**3.** What did you do at the store?
A. Two years.
B. I was a sales assistant.
C. This place looks great!

**4.** Can you make cabinets?
A. No, I can't, but I can learn.
B. OK, I can work Saturday.
C. Listen, I need a favor.

(Track 48) Page 111. Listen to the conversation. Then listen to the question and three answers. What is the correct answer: A, B, or C?

**5.** **F:** Can you work Friday from 1:00 to 6:00?
**M:** Uh, well, yes, I can.

When can he work?
A. Thursday from 1:00 to 6:00
B. Friday from 12:00 to 5:00
C. Friday from 1:00 to 6:00

**6.** **M:** How long were you a cashier at the supermarket?
**F:** Fourteen years.

How long was she a cashier?
A. four years
B. fourteen years
C. fifteen years